S0-AUA-440

612
GAB

Gabb, Michael

Human kind

	DATE		

© THE BAKER & TAYLOR CO.

Human Kind

FOUNDATIONS OF SCIENCE LIBRARY

The Natural World
(4 volumes)

The Majesty of the Heavens
(Foundations of Astronomy)

The Round World
(Foundations of Geology and Geomorphology)

The Skies and the Seas
(Foundations of Meteorology, Oceanography & Cartography)

The Ages of the Earth
{Foundations of Palaeogeography and Palaeontology)

The Biological Sciences
(6 volumes)

The Life of Animals without Backbones
(Foundations of Invertebrate Zoology)

The Life of Animals with Backbones
(Foundations of Vertebrate Zoology)

The World of Plants
(Foundations of Botany)

Breeding and Growing
(Foundations of Genetics, Anthropology and Agriculture)

Patterns of Living
(Foundations of Ecology)

Human Kind
(Foundations of Human Biology)

The Physical Sciences
(9 volumes)

The Restlessness of Matter
(Foundations of Aerodynamics, Hydrodynamics and Thermodynamics)

The Science of Movement
(Foundations of Mechanics and Sound)

Lightning in Harness
(Foundations of Electricity)

The Silent Energy
(Foundations of Electrical Technology)

The Cathode Ray Revolution
(Foundations of Electronics)

The Rays of Light
(Foundations of Optics)

The Unseen Spectrum
(Foundations of Electromagnetic Radiation)

The Cosmic Power
(Foundations of Nuclear Physics)

The Discipline of Numbers
(Foundations of Mathematics)

The Chemical Sciences
(4 volumes)

The Fundamental Materials
(Foundations of Basic Chemistry)

The Elements and their Order
(Foundations of Inorganic Chemistry)

The Giant Molecules
(Foundations of Organic Chemistry)

The Chemist at Work
(Foundations of Analysis and Laboratory Techniques)

Technology
(5 volumes)

The Metallic Skills
(Foundations of Metallurgy)

Industrial Processing
(Foundations of Industrial and Chemical Technology)

Engineering Technology
(Foundations of Applied Engineering)

Automobile Engineering
(Foundations of Car Mechanics)

The Inventive Genius
(Foundations of Scientific Inventions)

History and Reference
(3 volumes)

The Beginnings of Science
(Foundations of Scientific History)

Frontiers of Science
(Foundations of Research Methods)

A Dictionary of Scientific Terms
(The Foundations of Science Reference Book)

CHIEF EDITORS

Leslie Basford, B.Sc.   Philip Kogan, M.Sc.

ASSISTANT EDITORS

Michael Dempsey, B.A., Michael Gabb, B.Sc., Clare Dover, B.Sc.
Cyril Parsons, B.Sc., Joan Pick, B.Sc., Michael Chinery, B.A.
David Larkin, B.Sc., Paul Drury Byrne, B.Sc.

CONSULTANT EDITORIAL BOARD

Sir Lawrence Bragg, M.C., O.B.E., F.R.S., M.A., Nobel Laureate
Sir James Chadwick, F.R.S., Ph.D., M.Sc., Nobel Laureate
Norman Fisher, M.A.
Sir Harry Melville, K.C.B., F.R.S., Ph.D., D.Sc.
Professor J. Z. Young, F.R.S., M.A.

Human Kind

Foundations of Human Biology

MICHAEL GABB, B.Sc. MICHAEL CHINERY, B.A.

FOUNDATIONS OF SCIENCE LIBRARY
THE BIOLOGICAL SCIENCES

DISTRIBUTED IN THE U.S.A. BY
Ginn and Company : *BOSTON*
PUBLISHED BY
Sampson Low, Marston and Co : *LONDON*

This new presentation assembles
freshly edited material from
'Understanding Science' on one
subject into a single volume.

Copyright © 1966 Sampson Low, Marston & Co. Ltd.

SBN 356 00028 1

Library of Congress Catalog Card
Number: 66–18058

Catalog No.: L–20760

Made and printed in Great Britain by
Purnell & Sons Ltd., Paulton
(Somerset) and London

HUMAN BIOLOGY

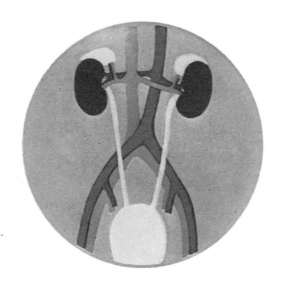

Contents

The Structure of
the Human Body

The Way Living Cells are Constructed

ALL LIVING things are made of cells. Apart from the very simplest animals which consist only of one cell, the cells that make up animals work together in groups. They do specialised jobs, carrying out the living processes of the animal. Groups of similar cells which work together are called *tissues*. Different tissues are united to form *organs*. All cells are held together in groups by cementing materials.

There are five main kinds of tissue. These are grouped as *epithelium* (lining and covering tissue), *connective tissue* (tissue which binds the organs together and packs the spaces between them), *skeletal tissue* (e.g. bones), *muscle tissue* and *nerve tissue*. The amount of cementing material between cells varies considerably between different tissues. Generally in epithelia it forms very little of the tissue and the cells are very close together, but in connective and skeletal tissues it may form the bulk of the tissue and the cells themselves are wider apart.

Lining and Covering Cells

An epithelium is a sheet of cells. The cells are held together by a small amount of cementing substance. The outer covering of the body (the skin), the lining of the gut and other organs,

An epithelium may be one or more cells thick and the cells may be of very different shapes and sizes. Some are thin and flat like crazy-paving stones. They form *pavement* or *squamous* epithelium which is found, for example, in the lining of parts of the kidney tubes. When the cells of squamous epithelium have wavy outlines (e.g. cells lining the blood vessels) they are said to be *tesselated*. Other cells are approximately as wide as they are tall. These form *cuboidal* or *cubical* epithelium which is found in many glands (e.g. liver). In *columnar* epithelium the cells are tall and column-shaped. Such epithelium lines most of the gut.

If columnar cells bear cilia the epithelium

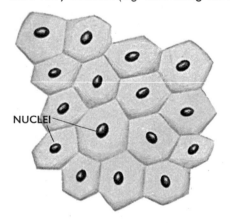

PAVEMENT OR SQUAMOUS EPITHELIUM

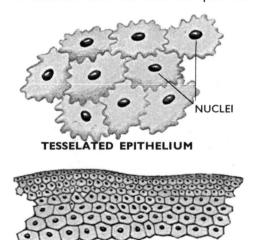

TESSELATED EPITHELIUM

STRATIFIED EPITHELIUM

such as the lungs and blood vessels, and the inner lining of the ducts in glands are examples.

Below most epithelia there is a thin sheet of connective tissue, the basement membrane. The free surface of most types of epithelium (the surface which is not attached to other tissue) may often have on it short hair-like structures called cilia.

When the epithelium is several layers of cells thick it is said to be stratified.

The cells of epithelia may serve very different purposes. Those lining the salivary gland and the glands in the intestine, for example, produce the chemicals (enzymes) which digest the food. The ones forming the outer covering of the skin are mainly protective, while the cells of the lung lining produce the wet mucus in which the oxygen dissolves before passing to the blood.

Binding and Packing Cells

Connective tissue is of tremendous importance to the body. It holds the cells of the organs together, supporting and surrounding them and passing on food to them from the blood, binds the parts of the body together and many of its cells are active in fighting and destroying disease-carrying organisms.

The cells in connective tissue are always well spaced in a thick fluid base substance or matrix, in which there may also be long, thin threads called fibres.

The most common type of connective tissue is called *areolar* tissue. It forms a layer beneath the skin and the lining of the gut and is also a packing material between muscles and other organs. It consists of a jelly-like matrix in which there are several kinds of cells and interlacing bundles of fibres. The fibres are of two kinds, white and yellow. The white fibres are very resistant to stretching but the yellow fibres can be stretched and are called yellow elastic fibres. Some of the cells are able to eat and destroy germs and so play a valuable part in the body's defensive system against disease.

Structural Cells

The skeletal tissues are *cartilage* and *bone*. They are often included with connective tissues as they have many similarities but the ground substance in them is solid whereas in connective tissue it is fluid.

Cartilage, or gristle as it is more commonly called, is rigid yet elastic. Its matrix contains very fine fibres and also cavities in which lie living cartilage cells. These produce the matrix

is then called *ciliated columnar epithelium*. Ciliated cells occur in the lining of the windpipe. The cilia beat to help remove dirt particles.

The outer cells of the skin and the lining of the cheek form *stratified squamous epithelium*. It is also found in the front, transparent layer of the eye (cornea).

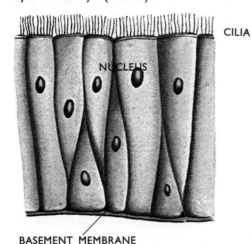

CILIA

NUCLEUS

BASEMENT MEMBRANE

CILIATED COLUMNAR EPITHELIUM

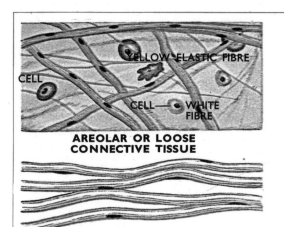

YELLOW ELASTIC FIBRE

CELL

CELL — WHITE FIBRE

AREOLAR OR LOOSE CONNECTIVE TISSUE

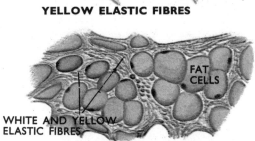

YELLOW ELASTIC FIBRES

WHITE FIBRES

WHITE AND YELLOW ELASTIC FIBRES

FAT CELLS

FAT OR ADIPOSE TISSUE

Some tissues consist almost entirely of white fibres. Examples of this *white fibrous* tissue are tendons, which join muscles to bones, ligaments which bind bones together at joints, and the protective coverings of organs such as muscles.

Yellow elastic tissue is made up mainly of yellow elastic fibres. The ligaments which hold the bones of the backbone together are yellow elastic tissue.

Reticular tissue is a connective tissue which occurs as thin sheets. It surrounds nerve and muscle fibres and also forms the basement membrane of epithelia.

Some connective tissue cells are able to store fat. Such *adipose* tissue is situated mainly in the deep layers of the skin and the mesentery (the thin sheet of tissue which holds the intestine in place).

Blood is often classified as a connective tissue. It consists of a *liquid plasma*, the matrix, in which float the *cells or corpuscles*. The cells are of two main kinds, red and white. The red cells are far more numerous (five million to every cubic millimetre compared with seven thousand per cubic millimetre of white cells) and contain the red chemical

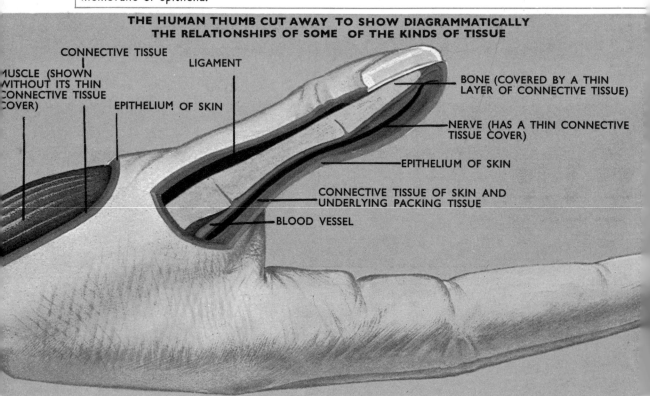

THE HUMAN THUMB CUT AWAY TO SHOW DIAGRAMMATICALLY THE RELATIONSHIPS OF SOME OF THE KINDS OF TISSUE

CONNECTIVE TISSUE

LIGAMENT

MUSCLE (SHOWN WITHOUT ITS THIN CONNECTIVE TISSUE COVER)

EPITHELIUM OF SKIN

BONE (COVERED BY A THIN LAYER OF CONNECTIVE TISSUE)

NERVE (HAS A THIN CONNECTIVE TISSUE COVER)

EPITHELIUM OF SKIN

CONNECTIVE TISSUE OF SKIN AND UNDERLYING PACKING TISSUE

BLOOD VESSEL

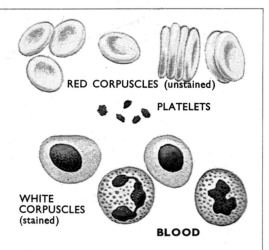

RED CORPUSCLES (unstained)

PLATELETS

WHITE CORPUSCLES (stained)

BLOOD

haemoglobin, which carries oxygen in the blood from the lungs to the tissues. Many of the white cells are able to engulf and destroy bacteria. Substances produced by the bacteria also kill white cells. These dead cells are familiar as *pus*.

Other small cells in the blood are called *platelets*. These play an important part in the blood-clotting mechanism and they also block any small holes that may occur in the blood vessels. There are about a quarter of a million platelets per cubic millimetre of blood.

which is constantly being renewed. It contains very few blood vessels.

Bone, unlike cartilage, has a very rich blood supply. The hollow cavity running through the centre of the long bones and the spaces in the other bones are filled with a fatty material called bone marrow. It is here that the red blood cells are produced.

Muscle Cells

Every movement we make is due to the pulling action of our *muscles*. There are three main kinds of muscle tissue, *unstriped* (also called unstriated, smooth or involuntary), *striped* (also called striated or voluntary) and *cardiac* or heart muscle.

Unstriped muscle is muscle over which we generally have no conscious control. Such muscle is found in the walls of the gut and the blood vessels. The size of the pupil of the eye is adjusted by involuntary muscles.

Striped muscle we can control at will. It makes up the bulk of the muscles in the body. Examples are the limb muscles, neck muscles and abdominal muscles.

Unstriped, striped and cardiac

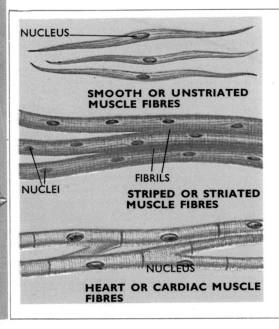

NUCLEUS

SMOOTH OR UNSTRIATED MUSCLE FIBRES

NUCLEI

FIBRILS

STRIPED OR STRIATED MUSCLE FIBRES

NUCLEUS

HEART OR CARDIAC MUSCLE FIBRES

Each unstriped muscle fibre is about $\frac{1}{5}$th millimetre long and $\frac{1}{150}$th millimetre wide and has a central nucleus. The fibre tapers to a point at each end. Smooth muscle is capable of slow, sustained contractions such as those that are needed to push the food slowly through the gut.

Each striped muscle fibre is about $\frac{1}{10}$th millimetre in diameter and may be several centimetres long. Each contains hundreds of nuclei and is made of long, thin strands or fibrils which appear striped with alternate light and dark bands. The width of these bands alters when the muscle contracts.

Cardiac muscle is found only in the wall of the heart. It is composed of fibres which branch and join to form an elaborate network. This arrangement is fitted for the muscle movement needed to enlarge and shrink the bag-shaped heart. The fibres are made up of fibrils and these are striped in a similar way to those of striped muscle. At intervals dark bands or partitions cross the fibres.

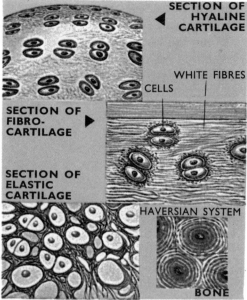

SECTION OF
HYALINE
CARTILAGE

SECTION OF
FIBRO-
CARTILAGE

SECTION OF
ELASTIC
CARTILAGE

WHITE FIBRES

CELLS

HAVERSIAN SYSTEM

BONE

The simplest type of cartilage is *hyaline cartilage* which is clear and glass-like. It joins the ends of the ribs to the breastbone and also covers the ends of bones where these rub together at joints. *Fibro-cartilage* is very tough and contains white fibres, but it is slightly elastic and forms the discs between the bones of the backbone and in the limb joints. *Elastic cartilage* contains yellow elastic fibres and is very elastic. The cartilage in the ear lobes and parts of the larynx or voice-box is elastic cartilage.

A *bone* consists of layer upon layer of hard calcium phosphate and other materials which form the matrix. In this are numerous star-shaped branching bone cells each of which is in a cavity of similar shape. The cavities are in direct contact with each other through numerous fine canals. Blood vessels and nerves lie in larger canals around which the bone cell cavities are arranged in rings. Each canal and its rings is called a Haversian system. There are many such systems in each bone.

muscle is made up of a number of units called fibres.

Nerve Cells

In the simplest animals each cell is sensitive to an outside stimulus. Higher animals, however, have specialised regions called receptors which are linked through *nerves* to a central switchboard, the brain and spinal cord. Information about the outside world passes from receptors to the brain or spinal cord. There it is translated so that the correct organ which is to act (e.g. a muscle) receives a signal through another nerve.

Nerve tissue, then, by passing signals from one part of the body to another, and in some parts storing information, is the body's main controlling agent. Not all the cells in the nerve tissue conduct signals, some form special types of binding tissue and pass food to the conducting cells.

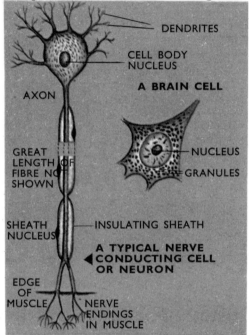

DENDRITES

CELL BODY
NUCLEUS

A BRAIN CELL

AXON

NUCLEUS

GRANULES

GREAT
LENGTH OF
FIBRE NOT
SHOWN

SHEATH
NUCLEUS

INSULATING SHEATH

A TYPICAL NERVE
CONDUCTING CELL
OR NEURON

EDGE
OF
MUSCLE

NERVE
ENDINGS
IN MUSCLE

The main part of a typical nerve conducting cell is the cell body. This is rounded but from .it branch a number of fine branches (dendrites) which receive signals from other nerve cells. A single fine branch, the axon, carries signals away to another nerve cell or to a muscle or gland. Axons passing from the nerve cord to the toes may be three feet long.

Each axon is a long thin thread of living jelly (protoplasm) surrounded by an insulating layer of fatty materials and protein. Every nerve fibre has a thin membrane round it. A small nerve is a bundle of nerve fibres surrounded by a sheath. Large nerves contain a number of bundles.

Not all nerve-conducting cells have a long axon. Many of the cells in the brain, for example, have one which is about the same length as the dendrites.

CHAPTER TWO

The Skeleton

JUST as a framework of girders supports a bridge or a building so the bony skeleton of Man and most other vertebrate animals carries the weight of soft body tissues. Without this internal skeleton the body would be practically helpless; it would collapse under its own weight.

The bony skeleton also helps to protect the delicate organs of the body. The brain is, for instance, enclosed by the cranium, the heart and lungs are shielded by a cage of ribs and the eyes are protected by tough eye orbits.

A third function of the rigid bone skeleton is as a foundation for muscle attachment. To raise an arm, certain muscles have to shorten their length. But the arm in fact only moves in response to this contraction, if one end of the muscles is securely fixed. The bones provide just this anchorage.

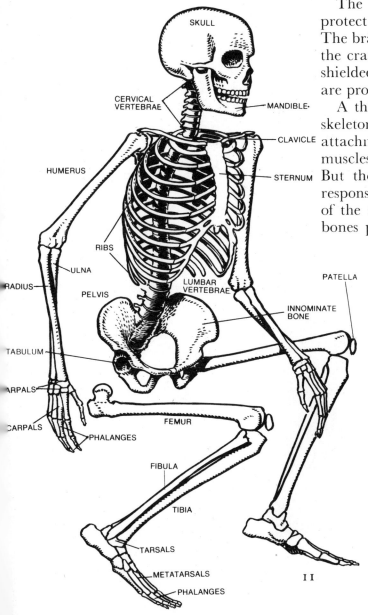

SKELETON

SKULL

CERVICAL VERTEBRAE

MANDIBLE·

CLAVICLE

HUMERUS

STERNUM

RIBS

ULNA

RADIUS

LUMBAR VERTEBRAE

PELVIS

PATELLA

INNOMINATE BONE

TABULUM

ARPALS

CARPALS

PHALANGES

FEMUR

FIBULA

TIBIA

TARSALS

METATARSALS

PHALANGES

11

CHAPTER THREE

Bone and Bones

THE mineral which gives bone its characteristic hardness and its resistance to decay is a complex calcium salt which contains both phosphate and carbonate radicals. But however solid bone may appear, nevertheless between 30% and 40% of its weight is made up of organic substances. There are in fact living cells within the bone supplied with minute blood vessels and nerves. The bones, of course, must be 'alive' for they could not otherwise mend after fracture or breakage.

Two different types of bone are distinguished by their mode of formation – the *membrane* bones and the *cartilage* bones.

Membrane Bones

The *membrane* bones have the simpler formation. They commonly develop in the *dermis* – the underneath layer of the skin. For this reason they have an alternative name – *dermal* bones.

Membrane bones develop (or *ossify*) when certain cells become bone-secreting. Such cells are called *osteoblasts*. The osteoblasts with numerous fibres of connective tissue cells, form an organic network. Then, into this network, layers of calcium salts (*lamellae*) are deposited. Slowly a plate is built up. The plate can grow about its margins and also can be thickened on either its inner or outer surface. Some of the osteoblasts remain alive and become actually incorporated into the growing bone. They are then known as *osteocytes* and come to have very irregular shapes. The spaces (*lacunae*) in which the osteocytes are situated are also irregular with long branching processes (*canaliculi*) extending in all directions. The canaliculi of neighbouring spaces link up and provide a network through which

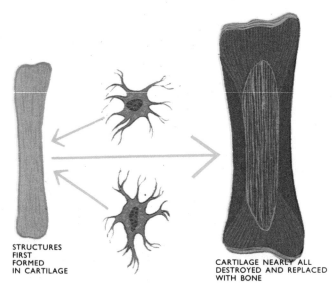

STRUCTURES FIRST FORMED IN CARTILAGE

CARTILAGE NEARLY ALL DESTROYED AND REPLACED WITH BONE

Bone may form directly *from special cells called* osteoblasts. *The structures formed in this way are called* membrane *or* dermal *bones. In some groups of vertebrates membrane bones form an outside protective bony armour.*

Bone may form when osteoblast cells invade structures already laid down in the embryo as cartilage. The result is cartilage *or* endochondral *bones. Most bones in Man's skeleton form in this way.*

blood containing food and oxygen can filter.

Cartilage Bone

Cartilage or *endochondral* bones in contrast to *membrane* bones are not formed directly. They are replacement structures – the bony material substitutes for early cartilage. What happens is that in the developing embryo most of the skeletal structure is first laid down as cartilage. This softer material is only gradually replaced by bone – a process which is not completed until the animal is full grown. In Man the ossification of the cartilage continues until the age of 25 or 26.

In shape the embryonic cartilage structures are miniatures of the final adult bones. They begin their transformation into the ossified structures soon after formation. First, the cartilage becomes calcified (impregnated with calcium salt) and many of its cells die. Then large amoeboid cells called *osteoclasts* penetrate into the calcified cartilage and begin to destroy it. They soon have created a series of channels and blood vessels break in. With the blood come osteoblast cells and bone begins to be laid down.

The cartilage of many vertebrates ossifies from one centre only. For instance the limb bones start to ossify in the middle and the process continues towards either end of the structure. The zone of ossification is called the *diaphysis* (DI-AF-E-CIS). In mammals, in addition to the diaphysis, other points of ossification may be set up. Each accessory point is called an epiphysis (EP-IF-E-CIS). Epiphyses are especially to be found on bony projections for muscle attachment or places which articulate with other bones. Thus, though ossification is incomplete as a whole, those parts which must particularly stand up to strain are already reinforced.

If the original cartilage did not grow, bone would soon replace all of it. But growth does continue. In the limb bones for instance, as fast as ossification takes place towards their middles, so new cartilage is formed towards the extremities. Only when the adult skeleton is completely grown

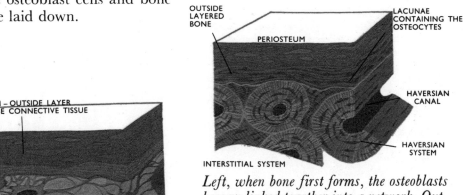

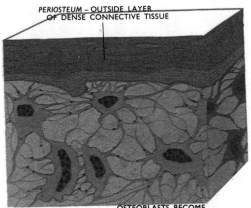

PERIOSTEUM – OUTSIDE LAYER OF DENSE CONNECTIVE TISSUE

OSTEOBLASTS BECOME OSTEOCYTES WHEN THEY ARE FINALLY SURROUNDED BY BONE. THE CAVITIES WHICH CONTAIN THE OSTEOCYTES ARE CALLED LACUNAE

OUTSIDE LAYERED BONE

PERIOSTEUM

LACUNAE CONTAINING THE OSTEOCYTES

HAVERSIAN CANAL

HAVERSIAN SYSTEM

INTERSTITIAL SYSTEM

Left, when bone first forms, the osteoblasts become linked together into a network. Outside of the bone is a layer of connective tissue the periosteum. *Right, reworking of bone forms the* Haversian *systems. Some of the first formed bone remain as chunks (the interstitial systems) within the Haversian systems.*

Cartilage is destroyed by osteoclasts. Osteoblasts invade and lay down bone (below). The change from the embryonic cartilage structure to the final adult limb bone is shown bottom right. Note the perichondral bone.

does cartilage stop developing; ossification is at last able to catch up.

The advantage of cartilage as an early skeletal tissue is that though less rigid than bone it can increase its volume from the inside. Bone, on the other hand, grows only by additions at its surface. There would be difficulties to the developing body. Parts of the bone surface are attached to muscles or are delicately articulated with neighbouring bones. Additional bone forming at the surface would disrupt these connections.

But nevertheless, the larger cartilage bones making the limbs are not entirely formed by replacement of cartilage. When ossification begins at an early stage, the cartilage structures are still very small in diameter. But later, the cartilage forming towards the extremities will be expanded in width. Bone replacing the cartilage produces a shaft that tapers towards the middle.

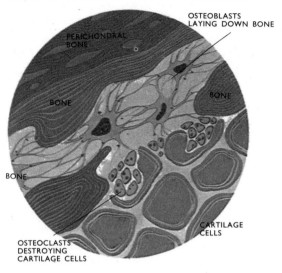

OSTEOBLASTS LAYING DOWN BONE

PERICHONDRAL BONE

BONE

BONE

BONE

CARTILAGE CELLS

OSTEOCLASTS DESTROYING CARTILAGE CELLS

COMPACT BONE – DENSE WITH CAVITIES MICROSCOPIC

SPONGY BONE – BONE MARROW FILLS THE SPACES

Bone varies in density, strength and hardness. The outer portions of bony structure usually consists of *compact bone* in which the percentage of living cells and organic substances is small. The inner surface of the larger bones is made of *spongy* bone. This consists of just a framework of bony bars giving rigidity; in between are fatty, vascular and other tissues forming part of the bone marrow. Spongy bone is light and lowers the overall weight of the skeleton without losing much of its strength. The very centre of the larger bones may become hollow. Replacing the bone are the soft fatty tissues of the bone marrow. The bone marrow itself has important functions – fats are stored and blood corpuscles made.

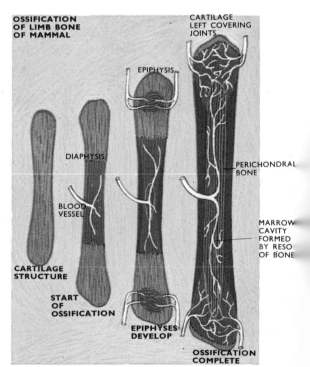

OSSIFICATION OF LIMB BONE OF MAMMAL

CARTILAGE LEFT COVERING JOINTS

EPIPHYSIS

DIAPHYSIS

PERICHONDRAL BONE

BLOOD VESSEL

MARROW CAVITY FORMED BY RESO OF BONE

CARTILAGE STRUCTURE

START OF OSSIFICATION

EPIPHYSES DEVELOP

OSSIFICATION COMPLETE

A bone shaped like an hour-glass would be very weak at its middle. The problem is solved by additions of bone to parts of the cartilage surface. The bone is particularly thick in the original, thin middle part of the structure. This coating of bone is, strictly speaking, membrane bone for it does *not* replace earlier cartilage. It forms on top of the cartilage and for this reason is called *perichondral* bone.

Throughout life bone is continuously being reworked. Old material is resorbed by the osteoclasts and new material deposited by osteoblasts. Re-modelled bones can be recognised in thin section under the microscope by the development of *Haversian* canals. The canals, which usually run parallel to one another, carry blood vessels and nerves. The blood vessels carrying food, pass out into the surrounding bone. Osteoblasts become arranged in a series of concentric circles about each canal. They rely upon the blood vessels in the canal for a supply of nourishment. Each canal with its dependent series of osteoblasts consti-tutes an *Haversian system*.

HEALING A FRACTURE

The body is equipped with the means to repair damaged tissue. The ability to repair and replace damaged or lost parts is not so great in Man as in many lower animals but, even so, considerable replacement may take place. For instance, practically the whole of the liver will regrow from only a tiny portion, large cuts and wounds will heal over to leave but a tiny scar, and the broken ends of bone in a fracture will reunite in such a way that the bone is able to take stresses again.

As soon as damage occurs, the body's healing processes come into play. This briefly is a description of the changes that occur when a bone is fractured. Following a fracture, blood seeps out of torn blood vessels and the gap between the fracture surfaces is filled up. The fluid is prevented from escaping by muscle tissue and the torn outer covering or *periosteum* of the bone. The blood clots to a jelly-like consistency so that the fracture is surrounded by, and filled with, a 'gluey' mass. This is called a *haema-toma*.

Slowly the haematoma becomes or-

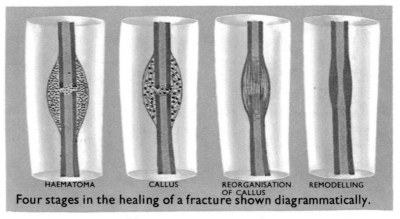

HAEMATOMA   CALLUS   REORGANISATION OF CALLUS   REMODELLING

Four stages in the healing of a fracture shown diagrammatically.

15

ganised. It is penetrated by fine capillaries that form a much branched network within. Gradually the tissue becomes firmer due to the deposition of calcium until it forms a rigid bond across the fracture. This *calcified callus*, as it is called, is invaded by bone cells. These absorb the calcium in the callus and replace it by bone. X-ray photographs at this stage show that the gap between the ends is filled with bone and the whole repair is surrounded by surplus callus. The new bone has yet to obtain its usual layered structure. Gradually it is reorganised, at the expense of unwanted callus, to take up the stresses that the bone has to bear. In children the remodelling is eventually so complete that usually no trace of the fracture can be seen in an X-ray photograph. Healing is never so complete in the adult and some thickening at the site of fracture is inevitable.

CHAPTER FOUR

Cartilage – the Body's Shock Absorber

A MAN running along the road crashes his foot to the ground with considerable force at every stride. Without bone or other skeletal support he could not do this for the force of landing would hopelessly compress the softer tissues of the leg. The skeletal tissues resist compressional forces acting this way. If the legs contained bone only, nasty shocks would be transmitted from one bone to another. This does not happen because another skeletal material – *cartilage* – cushions the joints and absorbs the shock. Cartilage is tougher and stronger than most connective tissue but not so rigid as bone. It resists both compression and extension.

Under the microscope cartilage shows up as a clear matrix in which are embedded numerous small groups of cells. These cells (*chondroblasts*) lie in fluid-filled spaces (*lacunae*) and secrete the matrix which is called *chondrin* (pronounced condrin). Compression forces are resisted mainly by the fluids in the cell spaces. The chondrin itself is slightly compressible and elastic and it absorbs shocks such as would be transmitted through the leg bones when a person is running.

Cartilage surrounding the ends of bones at their joints and lining the wind-pipe is known as *hyaline cartilage*. There are relatively few fibres in it. Fibrous cartilage, however, contains

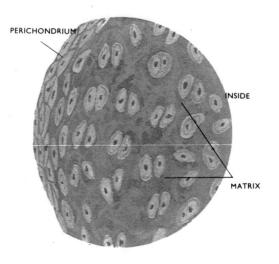

A section of cartilage tissue. At the outside the cells are close together. As they secrete chondrin they get further apart.

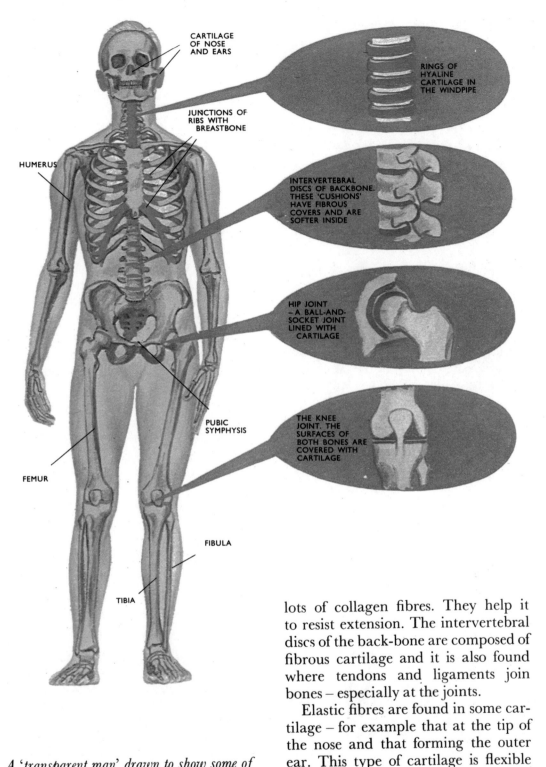

CARTILAGE OF NOSE AND EARS

RINGS OF HYALINE CARTILAGE IN THE WINDPIPE

JUNCTIONS OF RIBS WITH BREASTBONE

HUMERUS

INTERVERTEBRAL DISCS OF BACKBONE. THESE 'CUSHIONS' HAVE FIBROUS COVERS AND ARE SOFTER INSIDE

HIP JOINT – A BALL-AND-SOCKET JOINT LINED WITH CARTILAGE

PUBIC SYMPHYSIS

THE KNEE JOINT. THE SURFACES OF BOTH BONES ARE COVERED WITH CARTILAGE

FEMUR

FIBULA

TIBIA

A 'transparent man' drawn to show some of the positions where cartilage (blue) is found. It is also found in various tendons and ligaments where they join the bones.

lots of collagen fibres. They help it to resist extension. The intervertebral discs of the back-bone are composed of fibrous cartilage and it is also found where tendons and ligaments join bones – especially at the joints.

Elastic fibres are found in some cartilage – for example that at the tip of the nose and that forming the outer ear. This type of cartilage is flexible and is called *elastic cartilage*.

Each mass of cartilage (except at the ends of bones) is surrounded by a sheath of tough connective tissue called the *perichondrium*. This sheath contains blood vessels from which food materials diffuse out to the cartilage cells. New cartilage cells are built up from the cells of the perichondrium. Cells on the inside of this layer break away and gradually turn into cartilage cells. They begin to secrete chondrin and each group of cells becomes separated by the accumulating matrix. A section through the cartilage shows that the cells near the edge are much closer together and less specialized than the older cells near the centre.

CHAPTER FIVE

Muscles for Movement

WE tend to think of muscles only in simple terms, of organs that enable us to move from place to place or to lift or throw objects. In fact much of the energy unlocked when a muscle contracts is liberated as heat. This is particularly important in the warm-blooded animals, birds and mammals, for their high body temperature is largely produced as a result of the action of the muscles.

Muscles do not only produce movement. Some fix or hold parts of the body in place, giving the body its posture, acting as ties. Furthermore heart muscle moves the blood round the body; muscle in the walls of the blood vessels helps to control the supply of blood to various parts of the body; the pipes or ducts from glands contain muscle; and the muscle in the wall of the gut, by its rhythmic contractions, moves the food along and helps it to be digested.

The action of muscles may vary considerably. At one extreme the muscles of the arm and hand may work to enable a fast heavy blow to be aimed with the fist clenched, at the other the same muscles may act in a co-ordinated manner to enable the fingers to carry out the most delicate operations.

Over a third of the average vertebrate's body consists of muscle. Apart from heart muscle, there are two main kinds of muscle; these are *smooth* (involuntary or unstriated) and *striped* (voluntary or striated). We normally have no conscious control over smooth muscle, while striped muscle (the 'flesh'

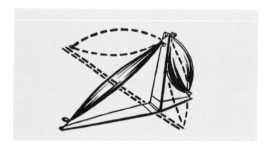

Balloons in a model show the working of the main muscles which raise and lower the human arm. When a muscle contracts its volume does not change.

The attachment of a muscle to a bone through a tendon. A muscle may be made up of several large bundles of muscle fibres, each bundle composed of smaller bundles of fibres.

of the body) can be controlled at will.

Smooth muscle includes the muscle of the gut wall, the walls of blood vessels, the lung tubes (these open out when we need large amounts of air during exercise) and the ducts of glands. It contracts slowly and can maintain this state for long periods if necessary. The muscles which control the size of the pupil of the eye, for example, keep the pupil a constant size when lighting conditions do not vary. On the other hand the slow rhythmic contractions of the gut muscles are ideally suited to moving food slowly through the gut.

Smooth muscle, then, is muscle that acts slowly but whose sustained contractions are of importance in holding organs in place, keeping the ducts of glands open or closed as required, and regulating the size of the blood vessels.

The fibres of smooth muscle are un-striped. As its name implies, striped muscle has striped fibres. This fundamental difference seems to be the key to the different actions of smooth

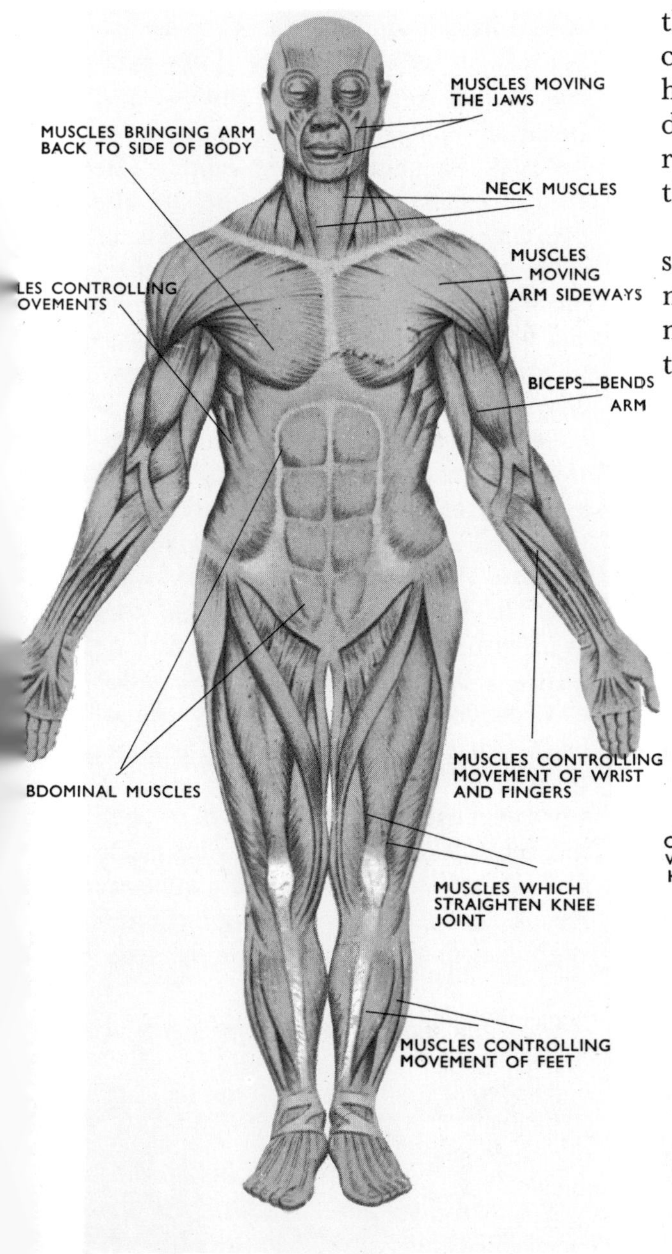

MUSCLES MOVING THE JAWS

MUSCLES BRINGING ARM BACK TO SIDE OF BODY

NECK MUSCLES

MUSCLES MOVING ARM SIDEWAYS

LES CONTROLLING OVEMENTS

BICEPS—BENDS ARM

BDOMINAL MUSCLES

MUSCLES CONTROLLING MOVEMENT OF WRIST AND FINGERS

MUSCLES WHICH STRAIGHTEN KNEE JOINT

MUSCLES CONTROLLING MOVEMENT OF FEET

NECK MUSCLES CONTROLLING MOVEMENT OF NECK AND HEAD

MUSCLES STRAIGHTENING SPINE

TRICEPS STRAIGHTENING ELBOW JOINT

MUSCLES CONTROLLING TRUNK MOVEMENTS

MUSCLES CONTROLLING WRIST AND HAND

GLUTEAL MUSCLES CONCERNED WITH THE UPRIGHT POSTURE

MUSCLES FLEXING KNEE

MUSCLES CONTROLLING MOVEMENT OF FEET AND ANKLE

Front View of Superficial Human Muscles. 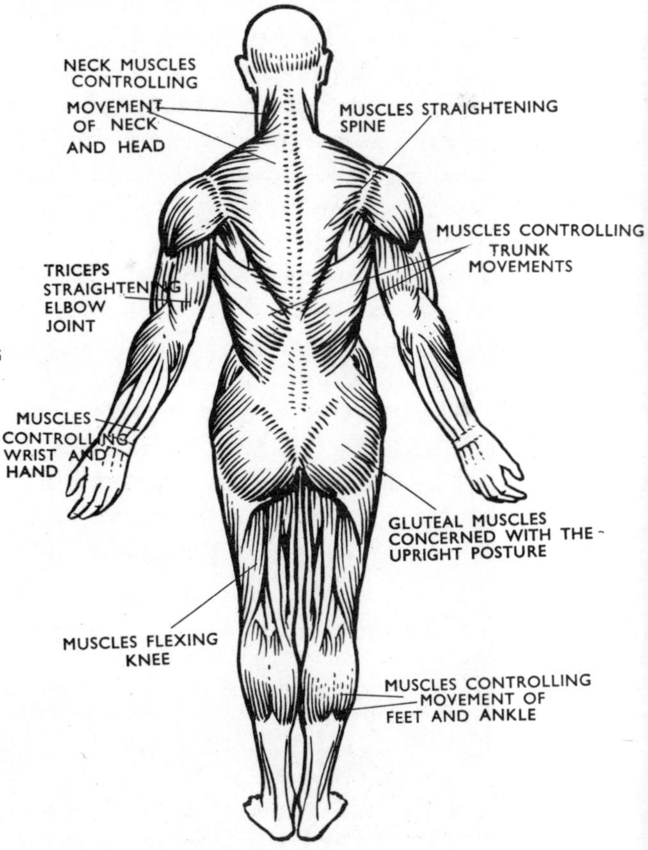   *Back View of Superficial Human Muscles.*

and striped muscle. The latter is able to contract very quickly to produce rapid movement. Its contractions cannot be sustained for such long periods as smooth muscle and it tires quickly.

Striped muscle is generally attached to the skeleton which it moves. Smooth muscle is usually arranged in coats or bands. When a muscle contracts it does not change in volume, even though its length may decrease. It may be compared with an oval balloon which has both ends pulled so that the balloon becomes thinner. Any reduction in the diameter of the balloon is compensated for by the increase in length, so that the volume of the balloon stays the same.

Muscles are attached to the skeleton by connective tissue fibres forming tendons or similar structures. Thus, when the appropriate muscle shortens, a part of the skeleton is moved. Muscles are not able to produce movement by pushing; they can only pull. They usually act in combination—a muscle rarely acts alone. One or more muscles act together to move a part of the body or to hold it in position, while other muscles act to pull in the other direction.

The fibres of voluntary (striated) muscles are of two kinds, *pale* (or *white*) and *red*. Both are present in varying proportions in all voluntary muscles. In some the white fibres

predominate, while in others the red fibres are more numerous. Generally speaking the pale fibres are more numerous in muscles mainly concerned with producing movement. They relax and contract rapidly, while muscles which are concerned with holding the body in certain positions against the force of gravity (the postural or anti-gravity muscles) contain mostly red fibres. They contract and relax more slowly and because of this are better suited for holding or resisting tension. The colour of red fibres is due to the presence of muscle haemoglobin or myoglobin as it is called (haemoglobin is the red pigment which gives the blood its colour and which carries oxygen from the lungs to the tissues). Myoglobin stores oxygen in the muscle and it is probable that this oxygen store is available for burning up the supplies of food (mainly sugars) in the muscle. As red fibres work slowly anyway this means that they are able to work for long periods too. White fibres, on the other hand, fatigue quickly, but they are able to do a lot of work in a short time. They enable us to run very fast, but only for short distances, for they have no oxygen store and use up the supplies of oxygen more quickly than they can be made available. This is why we can only sprint for a short distance, though with training this can be increased.

Muscles in the upper arm contract and pull on the bones in the forearm, so lifting it.

These arm muscles are relaxed when the arm is down.

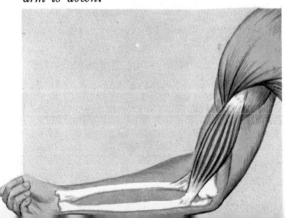

CHAPTER SIX

Nervous Systems

IN vertebrates, nervous tissue is concentrated at the anterior (front) end of the body, forming the brain. The vertebrate nervous system is characterised by this well marked *centralisation* and by the presence of large amounts of nerve tissue, by the actions of which the typical verte-

The Reflex Arc

When a sense organ (receptor) is stimulated signals pass from it along a sensory nerve to the spinal cord. The message travels out of the spinal cord along a motor nerve to the effector organ (e.g. a muscle or gland) which acts accordingly. Such a pathway is termed a *reflex arc*. The sensory nerve fibres of a spinal nerve do not enter the spinal cord at the same place as the motor nerve fibres of the same nerve leave the spinal cord. Sensory fibres enter the dorsal part of the spinal cord while motor fibres leave the ventral part. Sensory fibres are said to have *dorsal roots* and motor fibres have *ventral roots*. The cell bodies of sensory nerves are *outside* the spinal cord forming a swollen mass called a *dorsal root ganglion*.

brate behaviour patterns are controlled. While some parts of the brain are concerned with receiving signals from *receptor organs*, such as eyes and ears, and with sending signals to *effector organs* (muscles or glands), other parts are not directly concerned with receiving or sending signals and are not linked with any particular region of the body. These areas of the brain can over-rule the rest of the nervous system and so regulate the actions. In other words, these regions are responsible for the 'intelligence' of man, for his awareness of his surroundings and for the powers of learning. As one would expect, these *association centres* are more highly developed in mammals than in any other animals, and especially so in the apes and man.

The *central nervous system* (consisting of the brain and spinal cord) is hollow and situated above (dorsal to) the gut. This contrasts with the solid

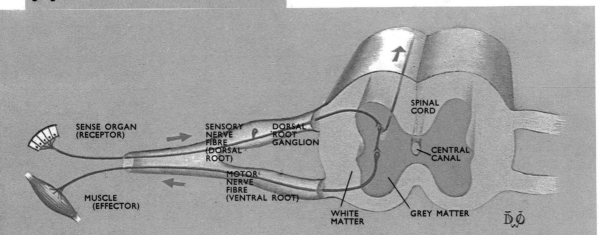

The section of the spinal cord and nerve shows the path of nerve impulses following the reflex arc.

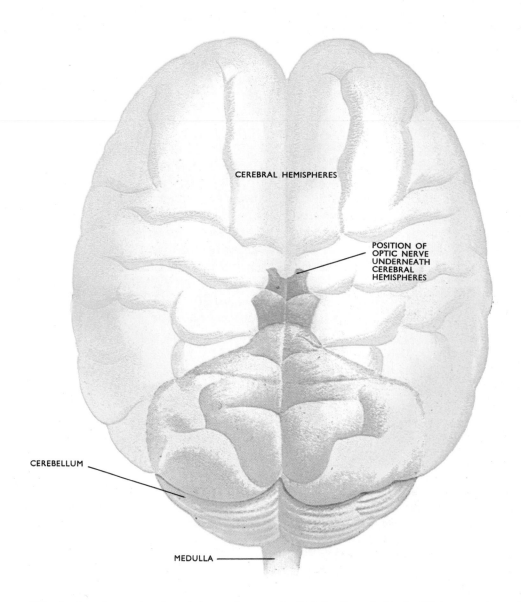

CEREBRAL HEMISPHERES

POSITION OF
OPTIC NERVE
UNDERNEATH
CEREBRAL
HEMISPHERES

CEREBELLUM

MEDULLA

The brain of man is viewed from above and slightly from behind. This, together with the ghosting of parts underneath the cerebral hemispheres, shows the positions and proportions of the fore-, mid-, and hind-brain. Note the backward extension of the hemispheres.

ventral nerve cord of the invertebrates. The vertebrate nerve cord and brain contain a liquid – the *cerebrospinal fluid* – which itself contains mineral salts and traces of protein and sugar. The fluid helps to support the nervous tissue and probably plays some part in its nutrition.

The mammalian brain is completely dominated by the cerebral hemispheres. The roof has developed enormously and spread out forming the *cerebral cortex* which in man is thrown into elaborate folds and almost covers the rest of the brain. The cortex is made up of millions of cells. The more folded the surface, the more cells it can contain. These cells make up the 'grey matter'. Their axons, which make up the *tracts* or pathways in the brain, form the *'white matter'* underneath the cortex. The *'white matter'* of the spinal cord is also made up of nerve axons, surrounding the central *'grey matter'*.

Most of the nervous functions in the mammal are taken over by the cerebral cortex. The cerebellum remains large and active, however, and the thalamus is enlarged for that is where the nerves of the sensory and motor systems link up and pass to and from the cortex where the messages are 'sorted out', 'stored' (i.e. remembered) and acted upon when necessary. The behaviour, both learned and instinctive of mammals, is controlled by the cortex. Each region of the latter controls certain aspects of behaviour such as sight, memory, speech in man, etc. Removal of any part of the cortex may produce definite changes in character or behaviour.

The diagram shows the peripheral nervous system of man. The brain and spinal cord form the central nervous system from which the peripheral nerves spread to all parts of the body.

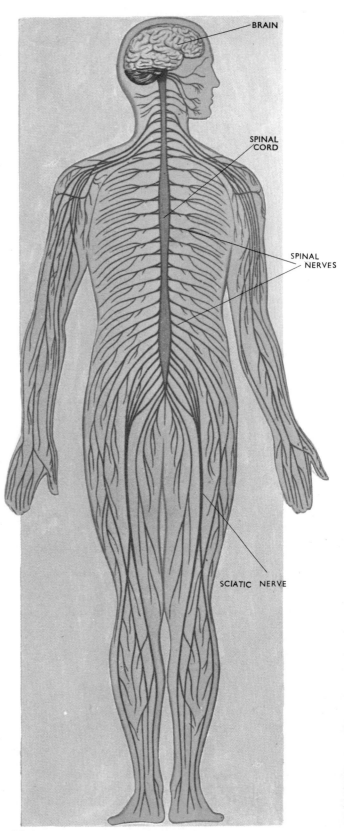

BRAIN

SPINAL CORD

SPINAL NERVES

SCIATIC NERVE

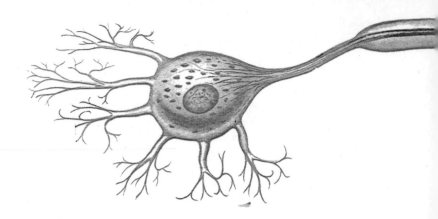

CHAPTER SEVEN

The Operation of Muscles by Nerves

MESSAGES from sense organs are transmitted to effector organs such as muscles by way of the reflex arc. This is the simplest case, where there are just two nerve cells (neurones) between sense organ and effector. The majority of movements however are the result of nervous messages passing along a chain of nerve cells. Between the sensory nerve and the motor nerves there are a number of connecting nerves called *association neurones*. These are not in contact with either sense organ or effector organ and merely pass on the nervous messages (*impulses*) to the next nerve in the chain.

An impulse is picked up by the fine branches (*dendrites*) at the end of the neurone and passes through the cell into the fine endings at the other end. These make contact with those of neighbouring neurones but the protoplasm does not join across the gap.

At the motor end plate the fine branches of the nerve come into close contact with the muscle fibres.

Motor nerve fibres may be very long. The dendrites of the cell body receive the impulses which then travel along the axon to the motor end plates of a muscle.

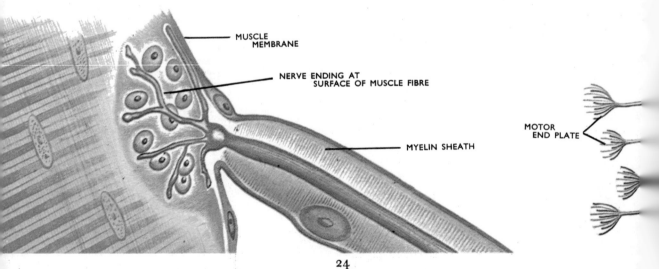

MUSCLE MEMBRANE

NERVE ENDING AT SURFACE OF MUSCLE FIBRE

MYELIN SHEATH

MOTOR END PLATE

The junction is termed a *synapse*.

When a receptor is stimulated (e.g. when hot water burns the heat-sensitive cells in your hand) an electrical disturbance is set up and transmitted in its nerve, as a series of electric currents which can be detected and measured by placing minute wires (*electrodes*) on the nerve concerned and connecting them to an amplifying device and a meter.

The nerve cell is covered on the outside by a thin sheet of tissue (a *membrane*). When the cell is at rest (i.e. when there is no current moving through it) the membrane allows potassium and chloride ions (charged atoms or groups of atoms) to pass in and out of the nerve but not sodium ions. The latter are very abundant in the surrounding tissues. Organic ions, negatively charged, balance the potassium ions in the nerve and create a negative charge on the inside of the membrane. The sodium ions create a positive charge on the outside and the difference between the two charges is called the *resting potential* and is of the order of 80 millivolts (eighty thousandths of a volt). When the nerve fibre is stimulated by the receptor the properties of the membrane are altered and sodium ions are allowed to pass inwards. When they do this they neutralize the excess organic ions within the nerve cell and cause a negative charge to occur on

the outer surface. Sodium ions on neighbouring parts of the surface then move along and the resting potential breaks down on the next part of the nerve fibre and the inflowing sodium ions set up a current there. In this way a current is set up all the way along a fibre. As the surface potential is destroyed in the process of conducting an impulse, the nerve fibre cannot conduct further impulses until the resting state has been regained by 'pumping' the sodium out of the nerve cells. The period required for this is called the *refractory period* and in human nerve fibre is about 2 thousandths of a second. Because of the need for this re-charging period the human nerve cell cannot conduct impulses more frequently than about 500 per second. In practice the frequency will be much lower, 50 to 100 impulses per second. The sense organ itself regulates the frequency with which it sends impulses. All impulses in a particular nerve fibre are of the same size. A stronger stimulus will cause more frequent impulses *not larger ones*. If a sense organ is stimulated it will produce a reaction in the nerve but unless the stimulus is large enough there will be no impulse. If an impulse *is* set up it will be complete and of the standard size. This is known as the *all or nothing* law of nervous conduction. The size of impulse does vary however with the condition of the nerve. A thick nerve cell will conduct a

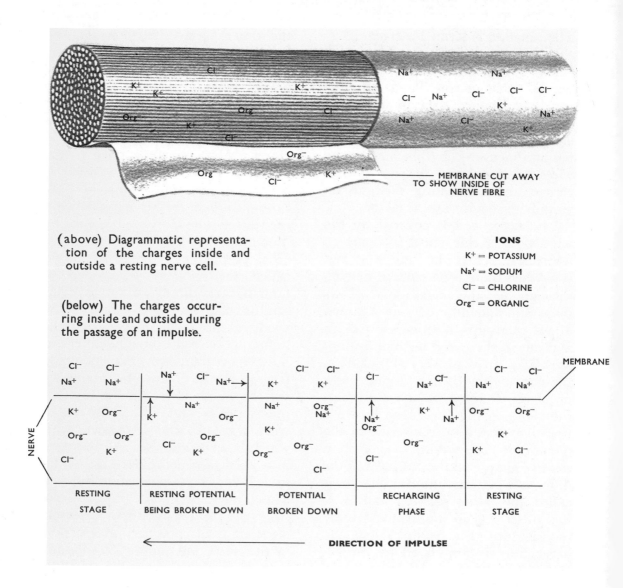

(above) Diagrammatic representation of the charges inside and outside a resting nerve cell.

(below) The charges occurring inside and outside during the passage of an impulse.

IONS

K⁺ = POTASSIUM

Na⁺ = SODIUM

Cl⁻ = CHLORINE

Org⁻ = ORGANIC

larger impulse than a smaller process of the nerve. A nerve fibre affected by drugs will also carry only a small impulse. The size of an impulse does not decrease as the distance travelled increases. It travels 'without decrement'.

On the way to the effector organ the impulse has to cross one or more synapses. A widely held theory concerning this mechanism is that when stimulated by the impulse, the nerve fibre ending produces a minute amount of a chemical called acetylcholine. This acts on the endings of the adjacent neurone and changes the permeability of the membrane. Sodium ions enter and the chain of electrical disturbances continues through this neighbouring nerve cell. As soon as it is produced, acetylcholine is attacked by the enzyme acetylcholine-sterase and is destroyed. If this did not happen the nerves would be 'poisoned'. Some of the powerful new insecticides destroy acetylcholine-sterase and so poison the nervous system of the insects.

When the nerve impulse reaches a muscle its electrical energy must be made to liberate mechanical energy in muscle contraction. Most of the work on contraction has been done with striped muscle which makes up most of the body musculature. The muscles are made up of large numbers of cells (fibres) each of which has one or more connections with a motor nerve ending. The junction between nerve fibre and muscle fibre is known as a *motor end plate*. A nerve impulse arriving at the junction causes the release of acetylcholine which affects the muscle membrane. Ions are allowed to pass in and out in much the same way as in nerve cells and the current

set up triggers off the contractile mechanism in the muscle fibre. Again the response is 'all or nothing'. When a single impulse reaches a vertebrate muscle fibre the fibre will contract and then relax. This response is called the *muscle twitch*. A series of quick impulses will keep the muscle fibre contracted since it will have no time to relax. This prolonged contraction is called a *tetanus*. *Tonic contraction* is the term applied to partial contraction of a muscle which can be maintained for a long

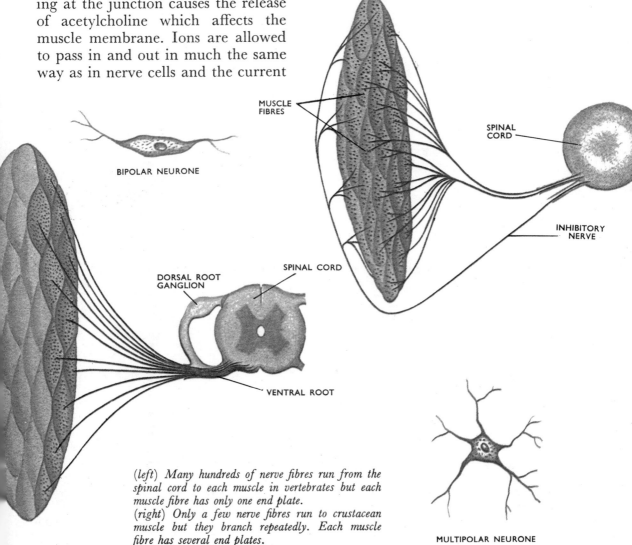

BIPOLAR NEURONE

MUSCLE FIBRES

SPINAL CORD

INHIBITORY NERVE

DORSAL ROOT GANGLION

SPINAL CORD

VENTRAL ROOT

MULTIPOLAR NEURONE

(*left*) Many hundreds of nerve fibres run from the spinal cord to each muscle in vertebrates but each muscle fibre has only one end plate.
(*right*) Only a few nerve fibres run to crustacean muscle but they branch repeatedly. Each muscle fibre has several end plates.

period. This is possible in striped muscle because there are hundreds of nerve fibres supplying each muscle. Each fibre branches two or three times and each ending supplies one muscle fibre. Impulses in a few nerve fibres will therefore cause only part of the muscle to contract. There is still complete contraction in each individual fibre affected. Tetanic contraction of striped muscle requires much energy, but tonic contraction of unstriped muscle can be maintained for long periods without fatigue.

CHAPTER EIGHT

Autonomic Nervous Systems

THE system of nerves spreading through the body is referred to as the *peripheral nervous system*. The *outer* or *somatic* part links up the sense organs that provide a 'picture' of the outside world, with the effectors that move the body towards food or away from danger. But in order that these sense organs and effectors function, the inner machinery of the body must be functioning smoothly and the rate

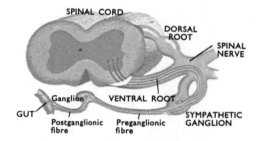

THE PATH OF SYMPATHETIC FIBRES OUT OF THE SPINAL CORD

Some of the Actions of Autonomic Nerves in Man		
Organ	Sympathetic causes	Parasympathetic causes
Heart	increase in rate and strength of beat	reduction in rate and strength of beat
Skin blood vessels	constriction	no supply
Blood vessels to muscle	usually constriction	no supply
Gut blood vessels	constriction	no supply
Muscles of alimentary canal (except sphincters)	relaxation	contraction
Sphincter muscles of gut	contraction	relaxation
Salivary glands	production of mucus	production of saliva
Pancreas	no supply	production of pancreatic juice
Hair muscles	contraction	no supply
Sweat glands	release of sweat	no supply

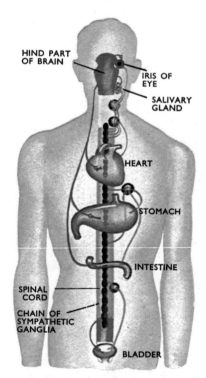

PARASYMPATHETIC NERVE FIBRES ARE SHOWN RED
SYMPATHETIC NERVE FIBRES ARE SHOWN BLUE

A simplified diagram of the human autonomic nervous system.

The cell bodies of somatic motor nerve cells are *inside* the spinal cord, but in the visceral motor system the cell bodies of the final motor nerve cells (those that are in contact with the organ that they supply) are *outside* the spinal cord. These cell bodies are grouped together to form ganglia that lie either close to the spinal cord along nerves or actually in contact with the organs that they supply. Thus, whereas the axon of a somatic motor neuron is long and carries impulses out from the spinal cord to the structure concerned, the typical visceral motor nerve is composed of two parts. One runs from the spinal cord to a ganglion and is called a *preganglionic neuron*; the other links with the preganglionic neuron in the ganglion and passes to the organ that it supplies. It is called a *postganglionic neuron*.

The preganglionic neurons usually have a fatty myelin sheath (they are *myelinated*), but the postganglionic neurons have no sheath and are said to be *unmyelinated*.

The autonomic nervous system may be divided into two parts, *sympathetic* and *parasympathetic*. Generally their actions are opposite and their positions in relation to the spinal cord are different (see illustration). Sympathetic nerves arise from the spinal cord between the neck and waist region. Parasympathetic nerves arise from the head and from the sacral region (between the waist and tail). Sympathetic preganglionic fibres leave the nerve cord by ventral roots as do somatic motor nerves, but parasympathetic fibres leave by both dorsal and ventral roots. Each preganglionic fibre is connected with many postganglionic fibres.

Though the two parts of the autonomic system arise in different parts of the spinal cord their branches spread nearly everywhere within the body. Most organs receive both sympathetic and parasympathetic neurons, though some (e.g. sweat glands) receive only one (in this case the sympathetic). The gut, for example (apart from the sphincter muscles), relaxes when it receives signals through sympathetic neurons. Signals through parasympathetic fibres cause it to contract. The sphincter muscles are affected in the opposite way, contracting on the receipt of impulses from the sympathetic and relaxing on receipt of signals from the parasympathetic. On the other hand the actions of the two systems may not strictly be opposite. The salivary glands produce a thick slime (mucus) when stimulated by the sympathetic system, but they produce the more watery saliva when stimulated through parasympathetic fibres.

The action of one system on different parts of an organ system may vary considerably. Signals from sympathetic nerves increase the strength and rate of the heartbeat, but the main arteries leaving the heart relax, so allowing an increased flow of blood. Sympathetic nerves usually cause the musculature of the rest of the blood system to constrict. During digestion the blood flow to the gut is increased by the gut blood vessels relaxing. At the same time the blood supply to the muscles is reduced to allow for this.

The actions of the autonomic nervous system are many and varied (the table lists a few). Experiments indicate that the sympathetic part is concerned with preparing the body for violent action and for withstanding abnormal conditions. The parasympathetic system is more concerned with re-establishing normal conditions in the body once it has been involved in strenuous actions, so that it is ready once more to expend large amounts of energy if necessary. Parasympathetic nerves initiate peristalsis (contraction of the gut) and stimulate the production of digestive juices by the associated glands. Parasympathetic fibres also supply the heart, lowering the frequency and strength of the heartbeat.

at which it works must be adjustable so that the varying demands of the outer structures may be satisfied. When moving the muscles require a greater supply of oxygen than when at rest. The heart must beat faster to supply more blood and this blood must be supplied with sufficient food and oxygen, the lungs must be filled with air and emptied more frequently, the blood vessels to the muscles must be expanded and more channels opened up there to cope with the increased supply of blood.

The nerves that co-ordinate the inner workings (e.g. smooth muscle of the gut and blood vessels, and the glands) form the *visceral* part of the peripheral nervous system. The *visceral motor nerves* are usually called the *auto-nomic nervous system* although they are controlled by the central nervous system just as the somatic motor system is. The autonomic nervous system is often referred to as the involuntary nervous system since we have very little conscious control of its activities, but with training it is possible to change the size of the pupil of one's eye or to increase the speed of one's heartbeat.

CHAPTER NINE

The Skin and What it Does

A FULLY-GROWN human being may have up to twenty square feet of skin. This skin, however, is more than just a boundary, more than just a covering for the underlying muscles. The skin is an essential organ performing a number of vital functions.

There are two distinct regions in the skin – the outer *epidermis* and the *dermis* underneath it. The innermost layer of the epidermis is the *Malpighian layer*. Its cells are living and divide quite frequently in a plane parallel to the skin surface. This layer contains pigment and is responsible for the colour of the skin. As the cells of the Malpighian layer divide, the outer ones are pushed towards the surface and become flattened. They gradually lose all their protoplasm and end up as horny scales which flake off as scurf. On some parts of the body, however, these cells build up thick horny layers (e.g. the sole of the foot). Hair and nails are outgrowths of the epidermis.

Underneath the Malpighian layer is the dermis. It is composed largely of connective tissue and, unlike the epidermis, contains many nerves and blood vessels. Elastic fibres in the der-mis give skin its elasticity but in old age, the skin loses this property and wrinkles develop. The upper layer of the dermis is irregular and the pattern is followed faithfully by the epidermis. This is why, if the outer skin of the finger-tips is damaged, the finger-

The skin contains a mass of elastic fibres which keep it taut and smooth. In old age (right) the elasticity fails and wrinkles appear.

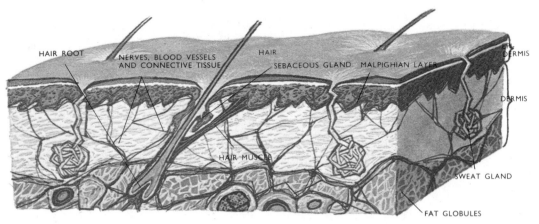

A section through the human skin showing the sweat glands and a hair follicle.

print pattern reappears and remains the same throughout life.

The Functions of the Skin

One of the most obvious functions of the skin is that of protection. Its elasticity is some protection against mechanical damage and its waterproof quality prevents excessive water-loss. The skin also prevents the entry of germs which could harm the body tissues.

A greatly magnified hair follicle showing the root and papilla.

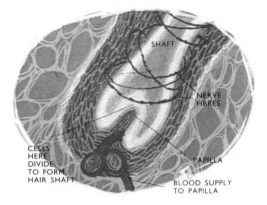

Temperature Control

Man, like birds and other mammals, is warm-blooded. His temperature remains constant within a degree or so of 98·4°F. The skin plays an important part in keeping this temperature constant. If, for any reason such as vigorous exercise or fever, the body temperature rises, the temperature of the blood reaching the brain will be higher. Nerve impulses are then sent out to the blood vessels and muscles of the skin. The vessels widen and carry more blood close to the skin surface and the blood loses heat to the air. This increased blood-flow produces a flushed appearance.

31

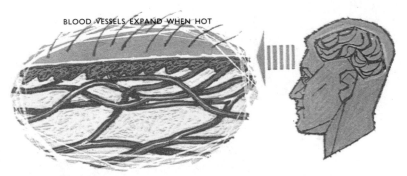

The skin is important in temperature regulation. When the blood is too warm, messages from the brain cause the blood vessels in the skin to expand. More heat is then lost. The vessels contract when it is cold and the skin becomes pale.

When the body-temperature falls, several changes occur. The chemical reactions within the body are usually speeded up to produce more heat energy. Shivering may occur – this is a subconscious act that, through mus-

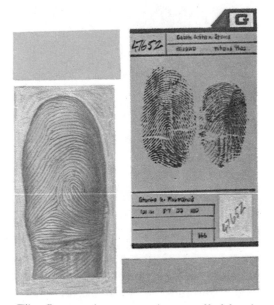

The finger print pattern is controlled by the underlying dermis. It remains the same always and thus can be used for identification purposes.

cular action, produces warmth. 'Goose-pimples' also may appear. These are more or less 'relics' from Man's early history. They are produced by the contraction of the tiny muscles attached to the hairs of the skin. Other mammals are able to fluff up their hairs by contraction of these muscles. This traps a thicker layer of air around their bodies and reduces heat-loss.

The blood-vessels of the skin contract when the body temperature falls and less heat is lost to the air. The skin is then pale for less blood is flowing near the surface. There is, however, another very important temperature control mechanism – *sweating*.

Sweating

A scientist named Kuno has estimated that the human body has perhaps three million sweat glands scattered over the surface, although they are more concentrated on the soles of the feet and in the palms of the hands. Sweat glands are tiny coiled tubes lying in the dermis and opening onto the skin surface. Water and various salts accumulate in the tube and pass out onto the skin surface where the

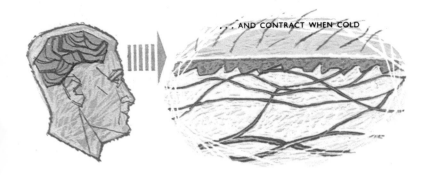

water evaporates. As a rule, it evaporates immediately and is unnoticed but the total cooling effect of the evaporation is quite considerable. In a humid climate, or during exercise, sweat may be unable to evaporate fast enough and beads of perspiration form on the skin. Sweating is controlled by the nerves and in cold weather the rate is reduced. The water and other waste materials still have to be removed, however, and this explains the greater number of visits to the lavatory in cold weather. The salts passed out with sweat are not all waste and include some sodium chloride or common salt. The salt content of the diet should be increased in hot climates.

Hair

Although hairs appear to come from the dermis they start in the epidermis. The epidermis grows down into the dermis to form tiny pits. They are found all over the body except the soles and palms. The pits, called *follicles*, have a bulge at the bottom rather like that at the bottom of a wine glass. Under the bulge is the hair *papilla* which feeds the hair. Cells at the base of the follicle divide repeatedly and the new cells are pushed outwards. They soon die but do not break off: the chain of dead cells forms the hair. The hair colour is determined by pigments. Its greasiness is caused by the secretion of the *sebaceous gland*.

Hair traps a layer of air between itself and the body and helps to maintain an even temperature. A tiny muscle attached to each hair can alter its position, although these muscles are very weak in Man. Hairs have tiny nerves around the base and are sensitive to touch. Some hairs have extra nerves and are extra-sensitive. The cat's whiskers are very sensitive to touch.

In cold weather, the muscles throw the skin into 'goose-pimples' to trap a greater layer of warm air (above).

Sugars such as glucose, maltose, lactose, and arabinose form osazones with phenylhydrazine. The osazones form as yellow crystalline solids. The inset shows the characteristic appearance of the crystals of three osazones. When the sugar is present in minute quantities the crystal appearance is affected by the presence of impurities (Crystals of glucosazone have a rounded rather than a 'needle-shaped' appearance).

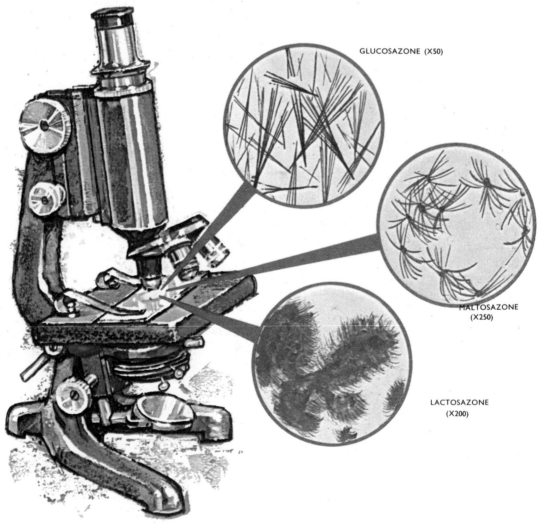

GLUCOSAZONE (X50)

MALTOSAZONE
(X250)

LACTOSAZONE
(X200)

The Need
for Food

CHAPTER TEN

Carbohydrates, Fats and Proteins

CARBON is familiar in nature as charcoal, diamond, and graphite. In these substances it occurs alone, uncombined with any other element. Life, however, is based upon the unique ability of carbon atoms to join together in long chains and in rings together with hydrogen and oxygen atoms and also with nitrogen, sulphur and phosphorus atoms.

Three main classes of carbon compounds are characteristic of plants and animals. These are *carbohydrates*, *fats* and *proteins*.

Carbohydrates

As their name suggests, carbohydrates are compounds that contain carbon, hydrogen and oxygen. The latter two are usually present in the same ratio as they are in water, namely two hydrogen atoms to one oxygen atom. Examples of carbohydrates are *glucose* (grape sugar), *sucrose* (cane sugar), *starch* and *cellulose*.

Carbohydrates (and fats) are to living cells what motor fuel is to the normal automobile engine. They are the main fuels that are burned to supply the energy needed to drive living processes. But they are not merely energy providers. In plants cellulose is produced in large quantities to form cell walls, and sugar molecules are often combined with non-sugar molecules to form *glycosides*. Examples of these are the *anthocyanins*, pigments that give blue, red and purple colours to flowers.

There are three main groups of carbohydrates, *monosaccharides*, *disaccharides* and *polysaccharides*. Monosaccharide molecules are single molecules of a simple sugar such as glucose. If two molecules of a simple sugar join together a disaccharide is formed. For example, a molecule of *sucrose* (cane sugar) contains one molecule of *glucose* and one molecule of *fructose* (fruit sugar). When many simple sugar molecules join together a polysaccharide is formed. A *starch* molecule, for example, consists of about two hundred glucose molecules joined together forming a chain. *Cellulose*, too, consists of chains of glucose molecules linked together in a slightly different way and also with linkages between neighbouring chains.

There are two main groups of monosaccharides:—*hexoses* and *pentoses*. Glucose is a hexose sugar. Its molecule contains six carbon atoms. Fructose is also a hexose sugar. Pentoses only have five carbon atoms in their molecule. (An example is *arabinose*). They occur in plants only in small quantities, but linked together and in combination with other substances they form polysaccharides and other compounds. The gums and slimes (*mucilages*) that occur in fleshy plants and seaweeds are examples.

Fats

Fats are compounds whose molecules contain only carbon, hydrogen, and oxygen atoms but the proportion of oxygen is less than that in carbohydrates. Thus, compared with carbohydrates a greater proportion

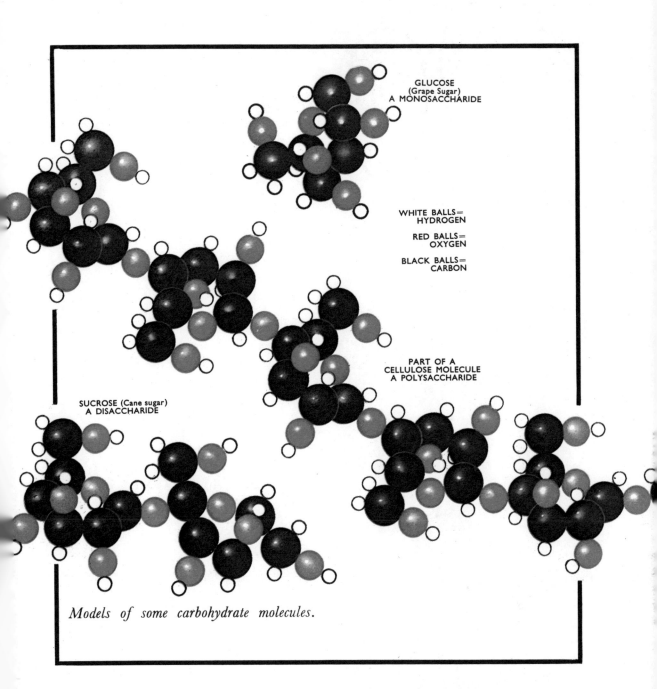

GLUCOSE
(Grape Sugar)
A MONOSACCHARIDE

WHITE BALLS=
HYDROGEN

RED BALLS=
OXYGEN

BLACK BALLS=
CARBON

PART OF A
CELLULOSE MOLECULE
A POLYSACCHARIDE

SUCROSE (Cane sugar)
A DISACCHARIDE

Models of some carbohydrate molecules.

of each fat molecule (the carbon and hydrogen part) can be burned. From the same weights of fat and carbohydrate more energy is released when the fat burns. Fat is, therefore, a greater source of energy than carbohydrates and it is extremely common in both plants and animals as a storage material.

Not only is more energy released when fat is burned (compared with the same weight of either carbohydrate or protein) but also more water is formed. This is of great importance to land-dwelling animals many of which live in conditions where water is in short supply. Burning fat is one way in which the

37

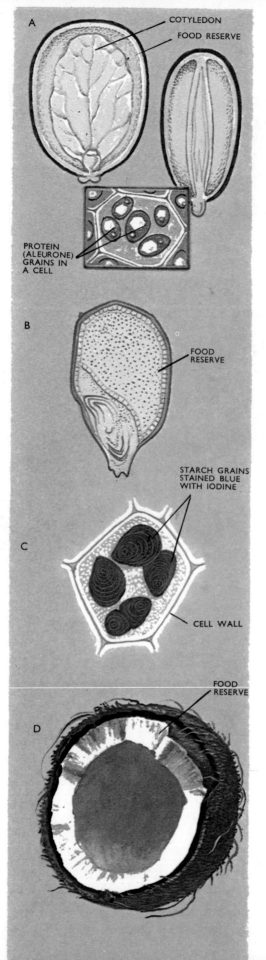

A. *Castor oil seeds contain oil and (inset) protein.* B. *Maize seed contains much starch reserve.* C. *Starch grains are also found in potato tubers.* D. *The coconut has a large reserve of oil and protein in its 'meat'.*

animal can add to the supply of water that it obtains as moisture from its food or by drinking. The hump of the camel is not a water tank as the popular stories would have us believe. It is in fact a fat store and the extraordinary ability of the camel to go for long periods without water is due to the fact that it burns its store of fat to obtain water.

Fats, then, are important as fuel reserves and their combustion supplies the tissues with a certain amount of water. They are also important in the structure of living tissues for appreciable amounts remain in the tissues even when an animal is starved for a long time. In vertebrates a fatty sheath surrounds nerve fibres and insulates them in much the same way that a rubber or plastic cover insulates an electric cable.

Chemically fats are esters (organic salts) of *glycerol* (glycerin), an alcohol that has three —OH (hydroxyl) groups, and a *fatty* acid. Fatty acids are formed in plant tissues by the oxidation of sugars, and it is probable that glycerine is also formed from sugars as well. An animal obtains some fat in its food. This fat is broken down by enzymes to fatty acids and glycerol whose molecules can pass through the gut wall, and the fat molecules are then rebuilt. But animal tissues can also convert sugars into fat. (We all know that 'starchy' foods such as bread and potatoes can cause us to grow fat!) Even so at least two fatty acids – linoleic and linolenic acid – are essential parts of a healthy diet.

Proteins

Fat and carbohydrate molecules contain only carbon, hydrogen and oxygen atoms, but proteins always contain nitrogen atoms and sometimes sulphur and phosphorus atoms as well. Their molecules are the most highly complicated of all substances because large numbers of atoms are present in each protein molecule in various different combinations and arrangements. This also means that the number of different proteins is quite astonishing – to the extent that every single living species has some which are peculiar to it and which are not found in any other species.

The importance of proteins lies in the fact that, together with water, they form the basis of all living matter or protoplasm. They also form part of the hereditary material that is carried on the chromosomes in all cell nuclei. Enzymes, the catalysts that are so vitally necessary for life, are proteins. Proteins are also used as food stores, particularly in the seeds of many plants.

Proteins may be compared with polysaccharides in that their molecules are built up of units. Many sugar molecules join to form polysaccharides. The units of which proteins are built are called *amino acids.*

The basic amino grouping of the amino acid molecule is able to react with the acidic carboxyl grouping of another molecule to form a *dipeptide.* Many amino acids can join end to end in this way forming long chains called *polypeptides* and eventually protein molecules. Each protein molecule is thus built up of large numbers of amino acids.

About twenty-five amino acids are known. To a limited extent animals are able to synthesize (*i.e.,* build up) some amino acids from simpler molecules. They are also able to convert some amino acids into others. However, a number of amino acids cannot be built up by animals or derived from others; they must be present in the diet and are called *essential amino acids* as distinct from the *non-essential* ones. Amino acids are able to combine in varying proportions and the same sequence of several amino acids or slightly differing sequences may be repeated many times so that a vast number of different proteins can be formed.

Proteins that occur in the nuclei of cells are called *nucleoproteins.* It is believed that the chromosomes are largely built up of nucleoproteins and some viruses have been shown to consist of masses of nucleoproteins. Thus certain nucleoproteins can be regarded as being the causes of several highly infectious diseases. It is also thought that the nucleoproteins of plant and animal cells are the

TWO SIMPLE AMINO ACIDS

BLUE BALLS= NITROGEN

The structure of glycine.

The structure of alanine.

makers of other proteins perhaps by making the enzymes that are able to piece together the necessary amino acids.

The important molecules (*nucleic acids*) in the nucleus that are arranged in strings on the chromosomes contain sugar molecules. The nucleic acids (principally desoxyribose nucleic acid, DNA), together with certain proteins, the nucleoproteins, form the basis of the hereditary material whose 'instructions' regulate all the activities of an organism.

CHAPTER ELEVEN

The Quality of Food

THE activities of the body are energy – consuming processes. The energy needed is obtained by the breakdown of the digested food materials by the action of enzymes within the cells of the tissues. Of prime importance as energy supplies are carbohydrates – starch, sugars and the like; of the other two basic food materials fats are more important as energy sources than proteins. The latter are primarily required for building new tissues and for repairing damaged or worn tissues, though under conditions of great stress – such as during serious illness – they may be respired in large quantities as can be seen by the wastage of muscle tissue.

Besides fats, carbohydrates and proteins, a balanced diet must contain traces of vitamins, mineral salts and, of course, water. Rich sources of carbohydrate are cereals, bread, milk, beans, peas, raisins, milk chocolate, syrup, jam and cakes. Fat-rich foods include butter, margarine, cheese,

The average adult doing light work during the daytime requires around three thousand Calories per day, represented by the whole circle. The diagram shows roughly how many Calories each major activity consumes.

1 *Calorie* = 1 *kilo calorie*

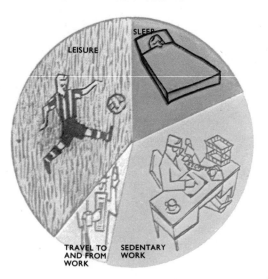

LEISURE

SLEEP

TRAVEL TO AND FROM WORK

SEDENTARY WORK

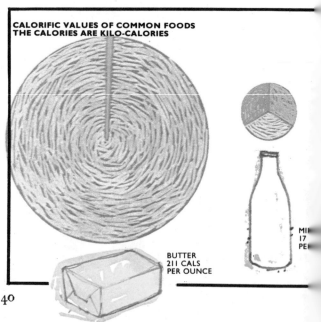

CALORIFIC VALUES OF COMMON FOODS
THE CALORIES ARE KILO-CALORIES

BUTTER
211 CALS
PER OUNCE

MI
17
PE

40

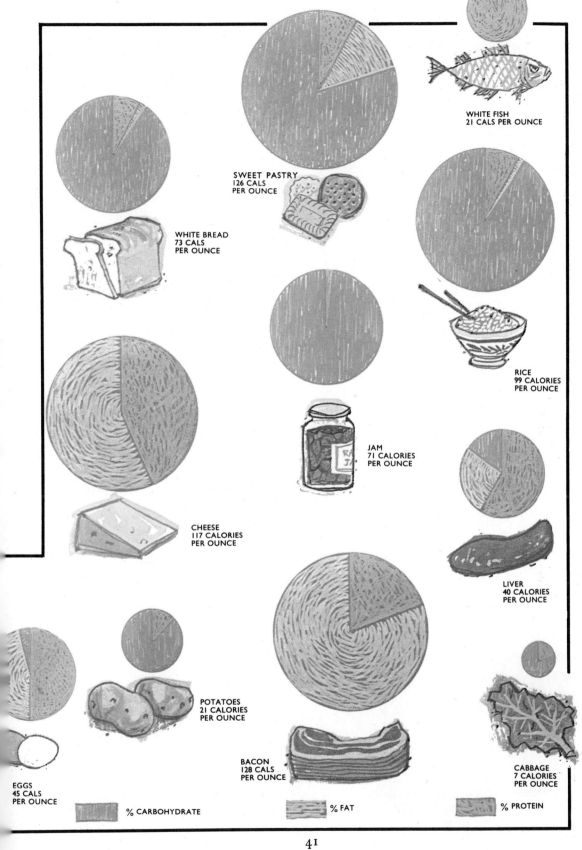

WHITE FISH
21 CALS PER OUNCE

SWEET PASTRY
126 CALS
PER OUNCE

WHITE BREAD
73 CALS
PER OUNCE

RICE
99 CALORIES
PER OUNCE

JAM
71 CALORIES
PER OUNCE

CHEESE
117 CALORIES
PER OUNCE

LIVER
40 CALORIES
PER OUNCE

POTATOES
21 CALORIES
PER OUNCE

BACON
128 CALS
PER OUNCE

CABBAGE
7 CALORIES
PER OUNCE

EGGS
45 CALS
PER OUNCE

% CARBOHYDRATE   % FAT   % PROTEIN

cooking fats, bacon, pork, peanuts and plain chocolate. Rich sources of protein are eggs, fish, meat, beans and peanuts.

The diagrams illustrate the varying proportions of the three basic food materials (fats, proteins, and carbohydrates) in various foods and also the number of calories that they yield per ounce. Foods such as sugar, which is all carbohydrate, are good energy suppliers, whereas milk and eggs are the best sources in animal protein. Foods rich in animal protein are better suppliers of proteins than plants because they contain a greater proportion of first class protein. Cereals are chiefly energy suppliers though wheat, for example, may contain as much as 14 per cent protein. Carbohydrates do and should form the greater part of the diet. When the diet is low in carbohydrate, fat is respired as the chief

The columns show the relative amounts of energy released by the complete combustion of 1 gm. of fat, carbohydrate and protein. Fat supplies more than twice as much energy per unit of weight as carbohydrate and protein.

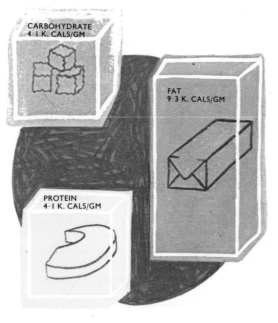

CARBOHYDRATE
4·1 K. CALS/GM

FAT
9·3 K. CALS/GM

PROTEIN
4·1 K. CALS/GM

Carbohydrates, which are made up of carbon, oxygen and hydrogen atoms, can be divided into two classes – the *sugars* and the *polysaccharides*.

Sugars are crystalline solids, sweet to the taste and soluble in water. The simplest of them – called *monosaccharides* – either have the chemical formula $C_6H_{10}O_5$ (the pentose sugars such as xylose) or $C_6H_{12}O_6$ (the hexose sugars such as glucose). Slightly more complicated are the *disaccharides*, which have their molecules made up of two molecules of monosaccharide (e.g. sucrose). Also found are *trisaccharides* and *tetrasaccharides* made up of three and four monosaccharide molecules respectively.

Polysaccharides are usually insoluble powders (e.g. starch, agar). Really they are gigantic sugar molecules for they are made up of hundreds, even thousands of monosaccharide molecules.

The digestion of carbohydrates is simply the breaking down of polysaccharides and disaccharides into basic monosaccharide molecules which can be dissolved into the blood stream.

Fats are esters (organic salts) produced by fatty acids combining with alcohols – usually glycerol. Like carbohydrates, they are also made of carbon, oxygen and hydrogen atoms. During digestion, fats are broken down into their components i.e. fatty acids and glycerol.

As well as carbon, oxygen and hydrogen, proteins contain nitrogen, sulphur and sometimes phosphorus. During digestion proteins first break down into fragments called *peptides*. These peptides, in turn break sown into the basic protein units, the *amino acids*.

alternative source of food, but this eventually leads to acidosis – an extremely high acidity of the body fluids. Fats are very economical storage materials, however. For every gram of fat that is completely respired, 9·3 kilo calories are yielded. The figure for 1 gram of carbohydrate is only 4·1 k. calories and for protein 4·1 k. calories.

CHAPTER TWELVE

Vitamins

BESIDES proteins, fats, carbohydrates, water and mineral salts, a healthy diet must include minute traces of substances called *vitamins*.

They are organic compounds whose absence from the diet produces abnormality of some functions of the body.

Our increasing knowledge of vitamins – the foods that they occur in, their chemistry and so on – has had widespread application. Many diseases which were thought at one time to be caused by germs are now known to be due to lack of certain vitamins in the diet. By encouraging people to eat the right kinds of food these diseases can be avoided.

One of the chief effects of vitamin deficiency is a slowing down of growth so it is important that children particularly should be well supplied with vitamins. It is during this ' early period that the human body is growing most actively and consequently the effects of vitamin deficiency will be most pronounced.

Plants are the ultimate sources of many vitamins for only they are able to build up the complete vitamin molecules from raw materials. Animals have limited capabilities in this respect and can only re-arrange organic molecules to make some of the vitamins that they require. The liver is able to make vitamin A from carotene, for example. Fish liver oils are a rich source of this vitamin.

Though we know the effects that lack of certain vitamins produce, little is known of the part that they play in the chemistry of living cells. Some are known to combine with protein molecules to form enzymes. Vitamin B_{12} (cyanocobalamin) helps in the synthesis of methyl (CH_3) groups. These occur in parts of the molecules of nucleic acids. Its lack slows the production of red blood cells in the bone marrow, and in old people results in the serious blood disease, *pernicious anaemia* (Addison's anaemia). Vitamin D is important in the body's metabolism of calcium and phosphorus. Lack of this vitamin seems to interfere with the normal ability of the body to take in sufficient

Crystals of vitamins highly magnified.

(1) B_1 (2) B_{12} (3) C (4) D.

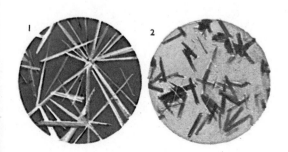
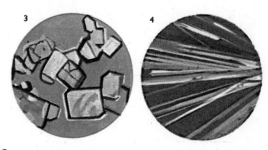

MAIN VITAMINS NEEDED BY MAN

VITAMIN	FOOD SOURCES	FUNCTION IN THE BODY	MAIN EFFECTS OF DEFICIENCY
A (Axerophthol)	Fish liver oils, butter, eggs, margarine, cream, green vegetables, carrots.	Growth and building of new cells. Associated with resistance of epithelia to infection. (particularly of eyes, gut and lung passages). Formation of eye pigments.	Xerophthalmia (hardening of cornea); Night blindness (poor vision in the dark); Dryness of skin; Poor bone growth.
D_2 (Ergocalciferol)	Fish liver oils, margarine.	Necessary for normal absorption of calcium and phosphorus.	Rickets; Osteomalacia (softening of the bones); Unhealthy teeth.
D_3 (Cholecalciferol)	Fish liver oils, butter, eggs, cream, liver, margarine.	Necessary for normal absorption of calcium and phosphorus.	Rickets; Osteomalacia (softening of the bones); Unhealthy teeth.
E (Tocopherols)	Wheat germ oil, green vegetables, eggs.	Necessary for proper development of foetuses and male sex cells. Prevents fats from being oxidized.	Inadequate nourishment of the muscles (muscular dystrophy). Loss of fertility.
K_1 (Phylloquinone)	Lettuce, kale, spinach, pig liver, tomatoes.	Blood clotting process.	Loss of blood clotting power. Excessive bleeding (particularly in new born).
B_1 (Thiamin)	Yeast, whole cereals, liver, eggs.	Important in carbohydrate metabolism.	Beri-beri.
B_2 (Riboflavin)	Milk, yeast, liver, wheat germ, meat, cheese, eggs, green vegetables.	Vital part in cell chemistry particularly oxidations.	Inflammation of the Tongue.
B_5 (Nicotinic acid)	Liver, kidney, meat, wheat germ, yeast, green vegetables.	Part of some enzyme systems; important in carbohydrate and protein metabolism.	Dermatitis (inflammation of the skin). Pellagra (disease affecting alimentary system, skin and nervous system).
H (Biotin)	Liver, kidney, egg yolk, milk, vegetables, nuts.	Necessary for the action of some enzymes (e.g. those causing breakdown of unwanted proteins).	Dermatitis; Muscle pains; Loss of appetite.
B_{12} (Cyanocobalamin)	Liver.	Necessary for formation of red blood cells, synthesis of methyl (CH_3) groups.	Pernicious anaemia (blood disease). Spinal cord wastes away.
C (Ascorbic acid)	Oranges, lemons, grapefruit, tomatoes, uncooked vegetables.	Formation of collagen. Healing of injuries.	Scurvy (bleeding of gums and other parts of body, painful joints).
Choline	Liver, pancreas, soya beans.	Fat metabolism. Synthesis of acetylcholine (substance released at nerve endings). Exchange of methyl groups between substances.	Cirrhosis (disease of the liver). Bleeding of kidney.

FAT SOLUBLE

WATER SOLUBLE

44

Many other vitamins have been discovered and are known to be necessary to other animals but have yet to be proved essential to man.

quantities of calcium and phosphorus. Thus the living cells of the bones and teeth do not receive sufficient supplies of these elements so that bones and teeth are poorly formed.

The effects of vitamin D deficiency are often obvious in children who eventually develop *rickets*. Providing the disease has not reached too advanced a stage, a complete cure is possible by administering cod liver oil, halibut liver oil or a food to which standard amounts of vitamin D have been added. Vitamin D is often referred to as the 'sunshine vitamin' for it is produced by the action of sunlight upon a chemical present in the skin.

CHAPTER THIRTEEN

Testing Foods

THE three main kinds of food substances – carbohydrates, fats and proteins – can each be identified by special tests. Most of these are chemical tests which reveal their characteristic chemical properties.

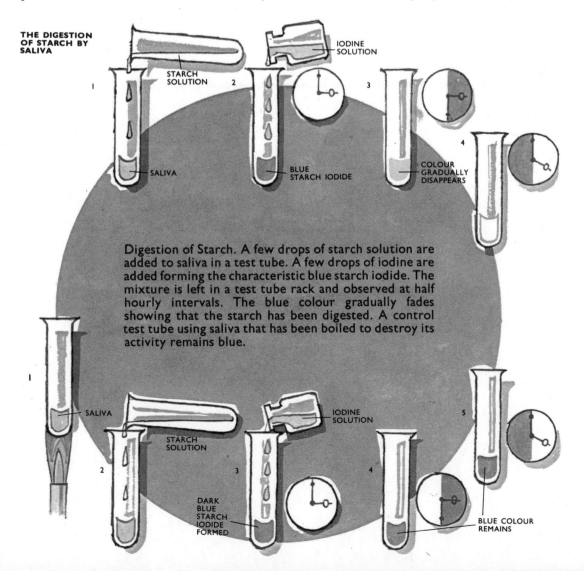

THE DIGESTION OF STARCH BY SALIVA

STARCH SOLUTION

IODINE SOLUTION

1   SALIVA   2   BLUE STARCH IODIDE   3   4   COLOUR GRADUALLY DISAPPEARS

Digestion of Starch. A few drops of starch solution are added to saliva in a test tube. A few drops of iodine are added forming the characteristic blue starch iodide. The mixture is left in a test tube rack and observed at half hourly intervals. The blue colour gradually fades showing that the starch has been digested. A control test tube using saliva that has been boiled to destroy its activity remains blue.

1   SALIVA   STARCH SOLUTION   IODINE SOLUTION   5

2   3   DARK BLUE STARCH IODIDE FORMED   4   BLUE COLOUR REMAINS

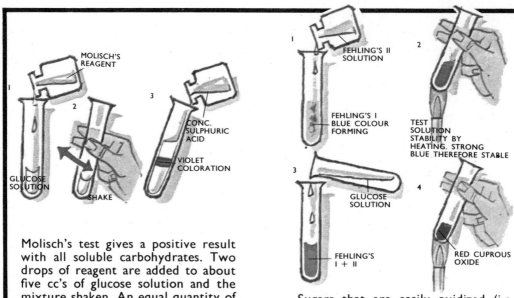

Molisch's test gives a positive result with all soluble carbohydrates. Two drops of reagent are added to about five cc's of glucose solution and the mixture shaken. An equal quantity of conc. sulphuric acid is poured slowly down the side of the inclined tube to avoid mixing. At the boundary between the two solutions a reddish-violet colour is visible.

Sugars that are easily oxidized (i.e. reducing sugars) reduce copper solutions with the formation of red or yellow cuprous oxide depending on the experimental conditions (speed of reduction etc). Typical reagents are Fehling's solution, Barfoed's solution and Benedict's solution.

FAT TESTS

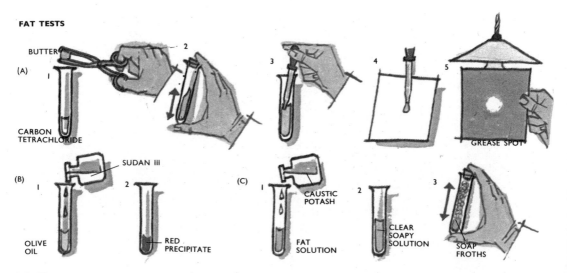

(a) *Fats give a grease spot if a drop of solution in a fat soluble material, such as carbon-tetrachloride, is allowed to evaporate.*
(b) *2 or 3 drops of Sudan III reagent yield a characteristic precipitate.*
(c) *The addition of caustic potash or other alkali to fat produces a clear soapy solution which froths on shaking. Soaps are the sodium or potassium salts of fatty acids.*

TEST FOR STARCH

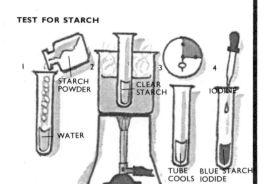

Test for Starch. The addition of a few drops of iodine solution to starch solution produces a characteristic dark blue starch iodide. Starch may easily be extracted from potato or a similar material rich in starch.

STARCH

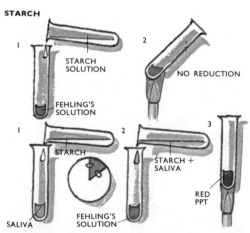

Starch gives a negative result with Fehling's solution but after it has been digested with saliva Fehling's solution is reduced showing that the starch has been hydrolysed to give a reducing sugar.

(a) A little eggwhite boiled with Millon's reagent gives a reddish coagulate indicative of protein.
(b) Eggwhite yields a white precipitate on the addition of a few drops of concentrated nitric acid. On boiling a

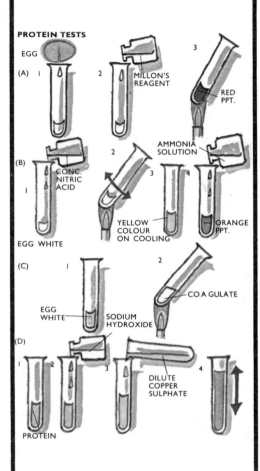

yellow colour results and if the mixture is allowed to cool and a few drops of ammonia solution added, an orange precipitate, indicative of protein, is formed.
(c) The nature of protein is destroyed by heat, giving a characteristic coagulate. This is what happens to eggwhite on boiling.
(d) *Buiret test.* The addition of very dilute copper sulphate solution to a mixture of equal volumes of protein 'solution' and sodium hydroxide yields a very pale pink to reddish-purple colour.

CHAPTER FOURTEEN

The Structure and Development of Teeth

AN adult human being normally has thirty-two teeth, sixteen in each jaw. The upper jaw has on each side two *incisors*, one *canine*, two *premolars* and, at the back, three *molars*. The same is true of the lower jaw. The number of teeth in an animal can be expressed quite conveniently by using the dental formula. This gives the number of teeth of each type in one half of each jaw reading from front (incisors) to back (molars). Thus the dental formula for man is $\frac{2123}{2123}$. For a rabbit, which has no canine teeth at all in its jaws, the formula would be $\frac{2033}{1023}$.

But man is an omnivorous animal (eating all types of food) and consequently our teeth are not highly specialised when we compare them with the grinding teeth of herbivores and the cutting teeth of carnivorous animals. Incisors are retained in most mammalian groups as chisel-shaped biting or cutting teeth. The canine is highly developed in hunting carnivores as a stabbing and tearing tooth. In man it is rather reduced and functions almost as another incisor. Many herbivorous animals have lost the canine tooth altogether. The premolars and molars of man are the grinding and chewing teeth. The surface of these teeth is covered with triangular or conical ridges (*cusps*) which fit into hollows of the opposing teeth when the jaws are brought together. Chewing movements then cause the teeth to act as millstones and grind up the food.

Although our teeth are modified for various purposes, they are all constructed according to a definite pattern. Projecting from the gum is the crown of the tooth. The part embedded in the gum and reaching into a socket in the jaw bone is known as the root. The body of the tooth is made up of a hard bone-like substance known as dentine. Inside this there is a cavity – the pulp cavity – which contains blood vessels and nerves. Branches from these, together with fine protoplasmic threads, penetrate the maze of fine canals which spread throughout the dentine. When the latter is damaged by decay or by the dentist's drill, the nerve endings are stimulated and we feel pain. Covering

The head of a six-year-old child showing the milk teeth position and the developing permanent teeth.

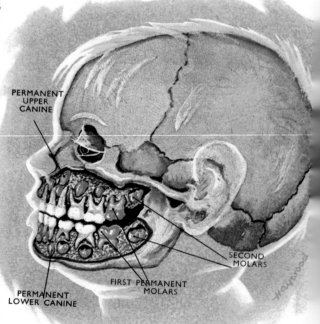

PERMANENT UPPER CANINE

SECOND MOLARS

FIRST PERMANENT MOLARS

PERMANENT LOWER CANINE

48

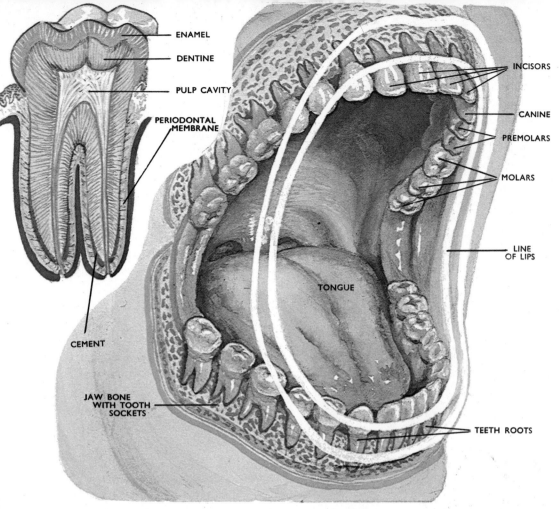

Mouth and jaws of adult human showing the position of the teeth. *Top left.* Structure of a molar tooth.

the crown of the tooth is a layer of enamel of varying thickness. It is made up almost entirely of *apatite* crystals with *calcium phosphate* filling. Apatite crystals are made up of calcium phosphate plus calcium fluoride or calcium chloride. Calcium phosphate is also mainly responsible for the hardness of dentine. The enamel layer crystals are elongated and are all arranged with their ends towards the surface of the enamel. Around the root of the tooth, enamel is replaced by *cementum* (the cement), another bone-like material which fixes the tooth firmly in the socket of the jaw. However, between the bone of the jaw and the cementum layer there is a layer of tissue – the *peri-*

odontal membrane which is in contact with the tissues of the gums and with the pulp cavity. Incisor and canine teeth have a single root, premolars have a double root and molars have three branches to the root.

We have seen that an adult has thirty-two teeth but a young child up to the age of about six has only twenty teeth. These are the *milk* teeth or deciduous teeth which are gradually replaced by the permanent teeth after the age of about six years. There are no molars in the milk set but the teeth corresponding to the premolars are known as the *milk-molars* and perform the same grinding function. The first milk teeth to erupt are the incisors which normally appear be-

49

Diagram of six stages in the development of an incisor from the bud to the fully developed tooth.

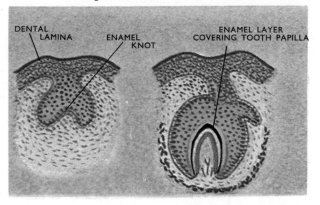

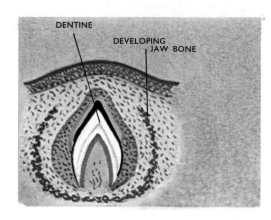

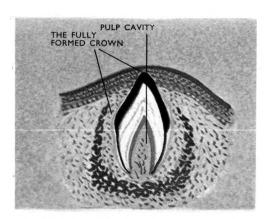

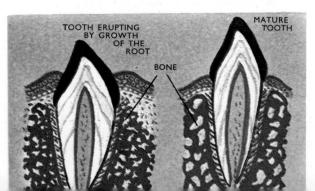

tween eight and ten months after birth. The full set does not appear until two years of age. The first *permanent* teeth appear at the age of about six years. They are the front molars. The milk teeth are then replaced by the permanent ones which grow up under them. Incisors are replaced first, then premolars and then canines, the latter appearing as permanent teeth at eleven years or so. The second molars appear at about 12 years and the third molars – wisdom teeth – not until eighteen or even later.

Human teeth are formed in the following way. In the early embryo the skin along the future line of the jaw-bones thickens and is known as the *dental lamina*. The edge of this extends into the tissues of the jaw and forms bud-like thickenings at intervals along the jaw. There are, at first, ten of these thickenings in each jaw. They are the 'buds' of the first set of teeth.

The dental lamina later extends beyond the last deciduous tooth bud and slowly forms the buds of the permanent molars. When the embryo is about three months old the dental lamina forms further tooth buds on the inside of the developing milk teeth. These are the buds of the permanent teeth. They develop in just the same way as the milk teeth but much more slowly.

The epithelial tissues of the tooth buds grow inward and form a bell-shaped structure in which a group of cells shows up densely and is termed the *enamel knot*. Under this knot, cells of the connective tissue become dense, forming the beginnings of the tooth body, the tooth *papilla*.

The cells of the papilla grow and multiply and push up under the enamel knot, forming a simple tooth-shaped structure. The cells of the enamel knot get larger and begin to produce enamel while some cells of the papilla start to release dentine. For the laying down of good hard material and its impregnation with calcium and other minerals, salts and vitamins – especially vitamin D – are needed in the blood. The hard layers are first deposited at about 20 weeks old by which time the bone of the jaws has started to form as a cup surrounding the developing teeth. More enamel and dentine are produced until the crown of the tooth is complete. The time required depends upon the type of tooth but when the crown is complete the tooth *erupts* (i.e. breaks through the gum surface) by growth of the root. The latter continues to grow for a while until it is completely enveloped in the jaw-bone which has grown up round it. Cement is produced by the tissues of the papilla when the root begins to grow. When the root is fully formed the opening of the pulp cavity closes so that very little food transfer can occur. Growth then ceases although the tissues still receive enough food to stay alive.

The permanent teeth continue to develop slowly under the milk teeth. When the crown of a permanent tooth is fully formed, its root begins to grow. This causes an increase in pressure on the base of the milk tooth. The result is that the periodontal membrane and the cement and even part of the milk tooth root are broken down by enzymes and by special scavenging cells which absorb the material rather in the manner of a feeding *Amoeba*. When the cement and the membrane have gone there is no firm attachment of the tooth to the jaw – the tooth in fact becomes loose and eventually falls out, leaving a clear path for the permanent tooth which now rapidly grows up through the gum to take its place in the adult tooth row. When it has reached full size and is firmly embedded in its socket, the tooth ceases to grow because the opening of the pulp cavity closes just as in the milk teeth. The gum is a mass of dense, fibrous tissue attached to the jaw bones. It is continuous with the periodontal membrane of the tooth socket which it supplies with food and oxygen via its rich blood supply.

CHAPTER FIFTEEN

The Fate of Our Food

IN humans the breakdown of the food begins in the mouth where it is mixed with the saliva. This watery fluid contains an enzyme, *ptyalin,* that acts on starch and converts it to a sugar, maltose. The tongue and the teeth help to break the large food particles down to smaller ones and thus ensure that as much of the food as possible is exposed to the action of

the ptyalin.

After the food has been mixed, partly digested and thoroughly wetted by the saliva, it is swallowed and passes down the oesophagus to the *stomach*. The food is moved through the oesophagus and the rest of the gut by the rhythmical contraction of the muscle in the wall of the gut. This is called *peristalsis*.

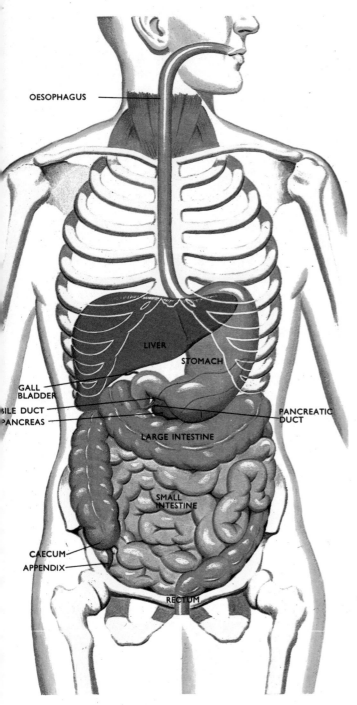

The stomach is a muscular bag that leads into a long, narrow tube, the *small intestine*. Where this joins the *large intestine*, there is a small blind tube—the *caecum*—at the end of which is the *appendix*. The large intestine leads into the *rectum* which opens to the outside by way of the *anus*.

In the stomach the food is sterilized by *hydrochloric acid* produced by cells in the stomach lining. Other cells release an enzyme *pepsin* which starts the breakdown of proteins. Another enzyme, *rennin*, clots milk by acting on the protein in it. The passage of the milk through the gut is slowed down. Thus more of the food value is extracted. This is of great importance in young children where initially the sole food is milk from the mother. Together with *mucus* (slime) the food is mixed in the stomach to form a paste called *chyme*.

A ring or *sphincter* muscle regulates the passage of food out of the stomach into the small intestine. The food has changed little chemically so far and only a small quantity has been absorbed by the stomach lining. In the small intestine many more enzymes are released and the chemical breakdown of the food is completed.

Various glands pour the fluids that they produce onto the food. The liver produces *bile* which enters the intestine through the bile duct. The *pancreas*, a gland between the stomach and the first loop (*duodenum*) of the small intestine, releases the pancreatic

The human digestive system.

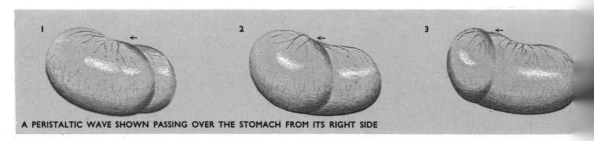

1   2   3

A PERISTALTIC WAVE SHOWN PASSING OVER THE STOMACH FROM ITS RIGHT SIDE

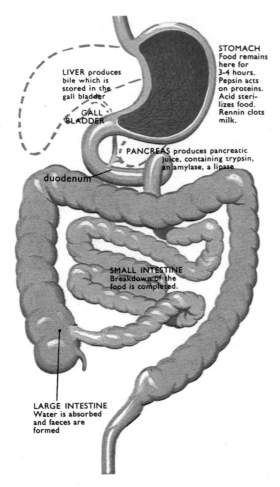

LIVER produces bile which is stored in the gall bladder

GALL BLADDER

duodenum

PANCREAS produces pancreatic juice, containing trypsin, an amylase, a lipase

STOMACH Food remains here for 3-4 hours. Pepsin acts on proteins. Acid sterilizes food. Rennin clots milk.

SMALL INTESTINE Breakdown of the food is completed.

LARGE INTESTINE Water is absorbed and faeces are formed

(Below) *A highly magnified view of three villi showing diagrammatically the network of tiny blood vessels and the fat-collecting vessels (lacteals) inside them.*

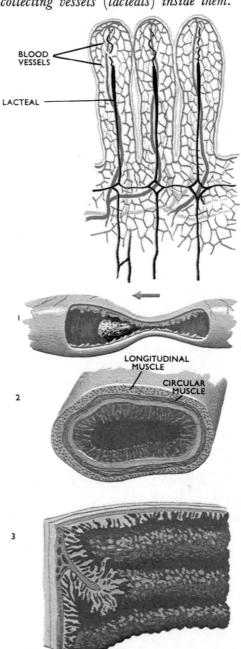

BLOOD VESSELS

LACTEAL

LONGITUDINAL MUSCLE

CIRCULAR MUSCLE

juice, an alkaline fluid that contains *trypsin*, an *amylase* and a *lipase*. Trypsin breaks down proteins to small units called proteoses and peptones, and these into smaller units made up of a few amino acids. The amylase breaks down starch into maltose (malt sugar), and lipase converts fats into fatty acids and glycerol.

The bile plays an important part in the digestion of fats. Salts that it contains (the *bile salts*) split up the

(1) *part of the intestine showing how the food is forced along by peristalsis;* (2) *the arrangement of the muscular coats of the intestine;* (3) *an enlarged view of part of the wall of the intestine to show the ridges covered with the finger-like villi.*

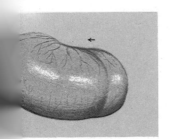

large fat droplets into smaller ones by lowering their surface tension—a process called *emulsification*.

Glands in the lining of the duodenum release an alkaline juice that contains a small quantity of an enzyme similar to pepsin. This juice and the pancreatic juice, together with the bile and the *intestinal juice proper*, make the chyme less acid.

The intestinal juice proper contains the powerful enzymes *erepsin*, a *lipase*, several *enzymes that act on carbohydrates*, and *enterokinase*. The latter acts on the *trypsinogen* (which has no action on the food) produced by the pancreas and converts it to *trypsin* (which breaks down protein). Erepsin breaks down proteoses and peptones to amino acids, and the lipase breaks down fats to fatty acids, and glycerol. Carbohydrates are broken into sugars.

The lining of the intestine is not smooth but it is thrown into a series of ridges or folds that are covered with finger-like projections called *villi* (singular—*villus*). Muscle cells are scattered through the interior of each villus and the wall of the intestine has two well-developed coats of muscle fibres. In the inner coat (circular muscle) the fibres run round the gut and in the outer coat (longitudinal muscle) they run lengthwise along the gut. The muscles of the gut are constantly contracting and relaxing, gently pushing the food along. Each villus contracts independently of the other villi about six times a minute, bobbing up and down like corks in a bowl of water. This helps to increase the efficiency with which the broken-down food is absorbed.

As the food moves through the gut, conditions there are continually changing. The food itself becomes more and more liquid as juices are added to it and as it is gradually broken down into smaller molecules that can pass through the gut wall. This is the main aim of digestion. The carbohydrate protein and fat molecules are too large to pass through the gut wall; they must be broken down into sugars (mainly glucose), amino acids, and fatty acids and glycerol respectively before they can be taken up by

DIGESTIVE ENZYMES AND THEIR WORK		
Region	Enzymes	Action
mouth	ptyalin in saliva	starch to malt sugar (maltose)
stomach	pepsin	proteins to peptones
wall	rennin	acts on milk protein
duodenum: from liver	bile	turns fat to droplets
from pancreas	trypsin	proteins to proteoses, peptones and smaller units
	amylase	starch to maltose
	lipase	fats to fatty acids, etc.
small intestine	erepsin	proteoses and peptones to amino acids
	lipase	fats to fatty acids and glycerol
	various enzymes acting on carbohydrates	break down carbohydrates into sugars (mainly glucose)

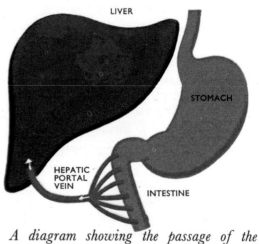

A diagram showing the passage of the digested food away from the intestine through the hepatic portal vein to the liver.

the cells of the body.

Absorption

Most of the absorption of food takes place in the small intestine. The large intestine is largely concerned with the absorption of water. This has been released as the main part of the fluids that help to convert the food to a liquid form so that it can readily be moved through the gut and is in a more suitable state for enzyme action. The passage of the food through the gut is eased by the production of mucus (slime). This also aids the formation of the *faeces* which consists of undigested food and, amongst other things, substances from the bile. The large intestine has no villi, but its wall has a rich supply of blood vessels that collect the water absorbed.

Amino acids and sugars are absorbed by the cells of the villi and pass from them into the blood capillaries there. These join to form the *hepatic portal vein* that carries them to the liver. Most of the fatty acids absorbed pass into spaces (*lymph spaces*) in the wall of the gut where they are built up into fats once more. Fat-collecting vessels called *lacteals* carry the fat to a main blood vessel entering the heart and it is distributed to the parts of the body that need it for fuel, or it is stored.

CHAPTER SIXTEEN

The Liver – Chemical Laboratory

THE liver is the largest gland in the body. In the embryo it arises as a pouch-like outgrowth from the gut, so it is to be expected that part of its activities is concerned with digestion. In the ancestors of the vertebrates it is likely that the liver was solely a producer of digestive enzymes. Though it still retains something of this activity in producing bile, its main functions concern the management of foodstuffs – fat, carbohydrate and protein – storing them and/or converting them into the molecules required by the tissues. Protein in excess of the body's requirements is broken down (*deaminated*), the nitrogen is converted into urea which is carried by the blood to the kidneys, and the remaining molecules are burnt to provide energy. Its other roles include the break-down of harmful or *toxic* substances, such as alcohol, the metabolism and storage of iron and copper, and the making of vitamin A (an activity that accounts for the rich supply of this vitamin in oils obtained from fish livers). It also produces heat, so helping to maintain the high body temperature. Special cells remove dead bacteria and the like from the blood. A recently discovered role is the storage of vitamin B_{12} (*cobalamine*) – a substance necessary for the proper formation of red blood cells. Lack of this vitamin causes pernicious anaemia. It is thought that the liver releases vitamin B_{12} when the level in the diet is low. It circulates in the blood, reaching the sites where red blood cells are manufactured.

The liver consists essentially of a series of five- or six-sided columns (*lobules*), each made up of chains of cells (*trabeculae*) radiating from the centre. Between the trabeculae are blood-filled spaces (*sinusoids*) and other

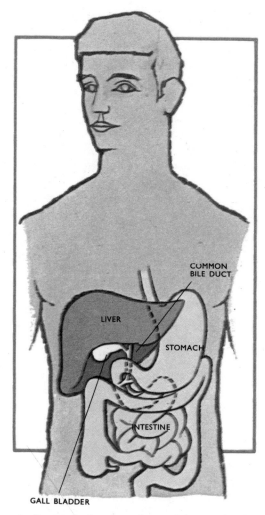

COMMON BILE DUCT

LIVER

STOMACH

INTESTINE

GALL BLADDER

A diagram showing the position and relative size of the liver in man, and the relationships of the gall bladder and bile duct with the small intestine.

'spaces' (*canaliculi*) into which bile is released. A blood vessel passes through the centre of each lobule. It collects blood from the sinusoids which are supplied by branches of the hepatic portal vein around the edge of the lobule. The central veins join to form the *hepatic vein* that carries blood back to the heart.

The liver is strategically placed in relation to the gut and the blood supply it receives from there. The gut itself has a rich blood supply to absorb the digested food material. Blood rich in food molecules is conveyed by way of the hepatic portal vein to the liver before it rejoins the main circulation. The liver, by a multitude of chemical processes, is then able to act on the food, before releasing to the tissues the substances that they require. This is also part of the activity by which the liver controls the composition of the blood.

The food materials arriving in the liver from the intestine obviously vary from one part of a day to another, and from day to day, depending on the quality of the food eaten. The activities of the liver will also vary, therefore, but not merely because of the food intake, for the demands of the tissues also vary from time to time. The muscles require little fuel while the body is resting, but, at a time when they are working rapidly, enormous supplies of fuel will be required. One of the principal activities of the liver in this respect is the storage of *glycogen* – a starch-like compound whose molecules are made up from numerous glucose molecules. When the blood contains more glucose than the tissues require, the liver cells join the glucose molecules together to form the larger glycogen molecules, and in this form they are stored. The liver is prompted to do this under the influence of *insulin*, produced by the pancreas. When the tissues require further supplies of glucose, the glycogen molecules are broken down and glucose is released into the blood stream.

The liver also stores fat. The latter can be broken down to release the energy needed to power chemical processes or to produce heat. The smaller molecules produced can be reassembled to form glycogen. Thus fats can be converted into carbohydrates.

In a similar way the liver cells can break down amino acids and convert them into carbohydrates. (They cannot build up amino acids from simpler units. Most of the amino acids that the body requires have to be taken in with the food). The amino ($-NH_2$) groups remaining are incorporated into urea molecules and this waste product is passed in the bloodstream to the kidneys for removal to the bladder. The liver breaks down only those amino acids that are surplus to the body's requirements for building up proteins and other molecules containing them. It normally passes on the amino acid molecules that it receives from the gut to the tissues that need them.

The liver cells release bile into the spaces (*canaliculi*) between the chains of liver cells. The tiny bile canaliculi join to form large bile channels that eventually join and enter the *gall bladder*. This is a 'pocket' that stores bile. Leading from the gall bladder is the *bile duct* which carries the bile to the intestine.

Bile is an alkaline secretion containing certain organic salts – the *bile salts* – the *bile pigments*, and such substances as *cholesterol* and *lecithin*. The bile salts reduce the surface tension of fats in the food, breaking them down into tiny droplets. This increases their surface area to such an extent that the fat-splitting enzymes in the pancreatic

Sugar molecules are carried from the gut to the liver via the hepatic portal vein. Excess sugar is stored in the liver as large glycogen molecules and released when required by the tissues. Each glycogen molecule contains many more sugar molecules.

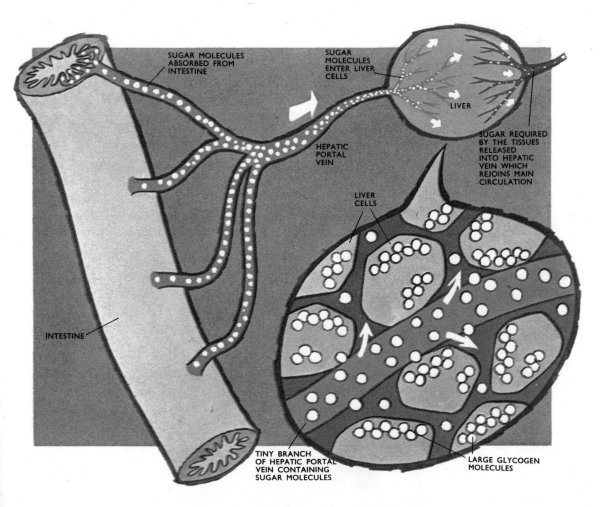

SUGAR MOLECULES ABSORBED FROM INTESTINE

SUGAR MOLECULES ENTER LIVER CELLS

LIVER

HEPATIC PORTAL VEIN

SUGAR REQUIRED BY THE TISSUES RELEASED INTO HEPATIC VEIN WHICH REJOINS MAIN CIRCULATION

LIVER CELLS

INTESTINE

TINY BRANCH OF HEPATIC PORTAL VEIN CONTAINING SUGAR MOLECULES

LARGE GLYCOGEN MOLECULES

juice can act upon them. The bile pigments are breakdown products of haemoglobin, the red colouring matter in the blood. The characteristic yellow colour of the skin in some kinds of jaundice is due to the retention of the bile pigments in the blood and in the tissues. This often results from a blockage of the bile duct. The same pigments give a similar colour to the faeces.

Apart from the production of bile and the management of food substances, a most important function of the liver is *detoxication* – the conversion of harmful substances into harmless ones by various methods. Thus ammonia, a highly toxic substance, formed in the process of *deamination*, is converted into *urea* for excretion by the kidney. A substance such as benzoic acid is combined with an amino acid – glycine – and converted to the harmless hippuric acid. Other substances are *acetylated*, that is, $-COCH_3$ groupings are added to the molecules. This is how the body gets rid of sulphonamides (a group of drugs). Associated with these processes is the removal of dead bacteria and other foreign matter by special cells – Kupffer cells. All may be considered protective functions of the liver.

The liver stores both iron and copper. It obtains iron from the food

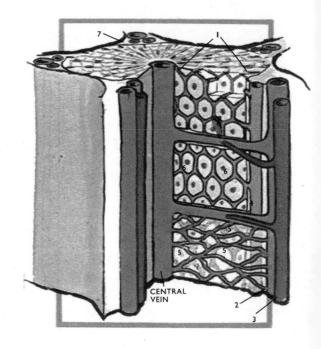

KEY TO DIAGRAM

1. CHAIN OF LIVER CELLS OR TRABECULA
2. BRANCH OF HEPATIC PORTAL VEIN
3. HEPATIC ARTERY (carries oxygenated blood to liver)
4. BRANCH OF BILE DUCT
5. LIVER SINUSOIDS – filled with blood
6. BILE CANALICULI
7. CONNECTIVE TISSUE ROUND LOBULE

A block diagram of a liver lobule cut away to show its internal structure.

and also retains that released during the breakdown of haemoglobin. Copper is not itself part of the haemoglobin molecule, but in some way it enables the iron atoms to be incorporated into the haemoglobin molecules.

Warburg manometers are used for measuring the gaseous metabolism of isolated tissues. Saline and tissue under investigation are placed in a special flask immersed in the water bath at a set temperature and connected to the manometer. Readings on the manometers indicate the gaseous exchange of oxygen and carbon dioxide. Analysis of the flask contents also indicates chemical changes that have occurred.

CHAPTER SEVENTEEN

"Living Fire"

GIVEN the right conditions sugar will burn fiercely, but in the living organism such uncontrolled, heat-producing (exothermic) reactions are of no use. The cell machinery is far too delicate to withstand high temperatures and such vigorous reactions would destroy it. The principal source of energy in the body is sugar (glucose rather than cane sugar) and the energy is released from it in a controlled step-by-step manner so that the cells do not blow themselves to bits or shrivel up through producing too much heat too quickly.

The chemical reactions within the body cells by which sugar is 'burnt' to release the energy needed to drive various other metabolic processes are controlled by catalysts called *enzymes*.

Some of the chemical pathways by which glucose is 'burnt' or respired

are known. This has been elucidated primarily by a painstaking series of experiments with 'juices' extracted from muscle tissue. Though the results of such experiments do not prove conclusively that this is what happens in living muscle – since chemical and physical distortion of the cell components must have occurred in obtaining extracts – it is very strong evidence.

Associated with these extract experiments are others on whole muscle – measurement of changes in oxygen uptake, carbon dioxide output, changes in the concentration of food substances such as glycogen, glucose, fatty acids and so on – all help to complete the picture of the metabolic activity of the tissue. Radio-active isotopes are also used as *tracers*. Coupled with these *chemical* techniques are *physical* methods of analysis which do not distort the cell chemistry in any way. These include the measurement of heat production, pH (acidity), electrical changes and volume changes.

The reserve of carbohydrate in muscle is *glycogen* or animal starch, whose large molecule is composed of glucose units. Pieces of muscle can be isolated and made to contract by electrical stimulation. Chemical analysis then shows that the store of glycogen has become depleted, oxygen has been consumed and carbon dioxide liberated. However, a muscle can be made to contract many times repeatedly in the absence of oxygen, until it becomes completely exhausted.

WATER BATH

MANOMETERS

Oxygen must then be provided for it to contract again. Under anaerobic conditions (oxygen lacking) it was found that large quantities of lactic acid accumulated in muscle and this also happens even during severe aerobic conditions.

The basic source of lactic acid is glycogen and it is produced by the hydrolysis of glycogen through enzyme action with the production of energy as heat and for doing mechanical work. The lactic acid disappears from the muscle when oxygen is admitted and heat is produced. The energy released by the oxidation of one fourth of the accumulated lactic

acid is sufficient to reconvert the remaining four-fifths back into glycogen. In this way there is a readily available store of energy for immediate use, and after exercise the store can be recharged by slower, less violent oxidation of lactic acid.

This briefly was our knowledge of the chemistry of muscle contraction around 1920. From more recent work we know that lactic acid is not actually formed during the actual contraction process but afterwards (it is this build up of lactic acid that produces the characteristic 'stiff' feeling some hours after taking violent exercise). Athletic training speeds up the processes by

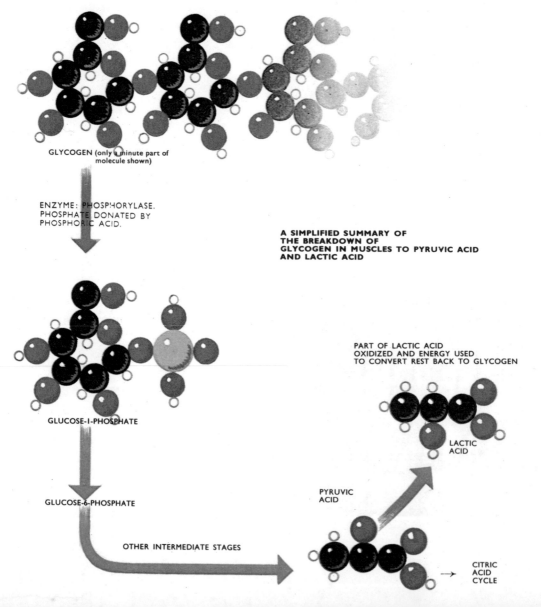

GLYCOGEN (only a minute part of molecule shown)

ENZYME: PHOSPHORYLASE.
PHOSPHATE DONATED BY
PHOSPHORIC ACID.

A SIMPLIFIED SUMMARY OF
THE BREAKDOWN OF
GLYCOGEN IN MUSCLES TO PYRUVIC ACID
AND LACTIC ACID

GLUCOSE-1-PHOSPHATE

GLUCOSE-6-PHOSPHATE

OTHER INTERMEDIATE STAGES

PART OF LACTIC ACID
OXIDIZED AND ENERGY USED
TO CONVERT REST BACK TO GLYCOGEN

LACTIC ACID

PYRUVIC ACID

CITRIC ACID CYCLE

which some of the lactic acid is oxidized to supply the energy for converting the remainder back to glycogen; thus little or no stiffness results in the fit athlete.

We now know that the primary end product of the hydrolysis of glycogen by which the energy for muscular contraction is supplied, is *pyruvic acid* and not lactic acid. Lactic acid only accumulates from pyruvic acid when the demand for oxygen during exercise is greater than the supply – that is under anaerobic conditions.

The change from glycogen through glucose to pyruvic acid takes place in eleven distinct steps. Each step (except one which proceeds of its own accord) is controlled by an enzyme. Firstly the links between the 'glucose' units that make up the glycogen molecule are broken by hydrolysis and each unit is phosphorylated – i.e. has a phosphate group added to it – to glucose-1-phosphate. Via a succession of such phosphate compounds eventually pyruvic acid is formed. Under aerobic conditions pyruvic acid is quickly 'absorbed' into another process – the *citric acid cycle*. This cycle, besides removing a waste product, also supplies hydrogen necessary for the reduction of certain cell constituents which have been oxidized while taking part in the hydrolysis of glycogen and other processes.

The energy for muscle contraction comes largely from the breakdown of glycogen to pyruvic acid. Six-carbon units are broken off from the long glycogen chain, and in the presence of phosphoric acid and the enzyme phosphorylase are converted to glucose-1-phosphate, then to glucose-6-phosphate by the enzyme phosphoglucomutase.

Glucose-6-phosphate is now converted, via many intermediate compounds, to pyruvic acid, and this is then incorporated into the Citric Acid Cycle.

The changes from glucose-6-phosphate to pyruvic acid and those in the Citric Acid Cycle release energy which is stored in a compound called Adenosine Triphosphate (A.T.P.), and this energy can be made available to muscles when A.T.P. changes to A.D.P. (Adenosine Diphosphate) + phosphate. In order to re-form A.T.P. from A.D.P. + phosphate energy must be given to it. It is also thought that another organic phosphate compound – *creatine phosphate* – is actively concerned with this, using some of the energy released by the change of A.T.P. to A.D.P.

Creatine phosphate splits, yielding creatine and phosphoric acid, which provides the 'phosphate' in A.T.P. A startling discovery made recently is that the enzyme that catalyzes the breakdown of A.T.P. is in fact the actual protein fibre which makes up the bulk of muscle tissue and which contracts – so causing the muscle to shorten.

The breakdown of glycogen provides the energy to recharge the muscle. It is an anaerobic process – one not requiring free oxygen. In this way an *oxygen debt* of around 20 litres can be withstood. The products of this process, pyruvic acid and lactic acid, are oxidized aerobically yielding energy and glycogen so paying off the oxygen debt. The fact that there is a limit to the oxygen debt that can be withstood explains why it is only possible to sprint flat out for short distances.

A portion of the energy released in muscle contraction is available as heat and it is primarily this source of heat which maintains the temperature of the blood above that of the surroundings.

Similar analysis of other tissues shows that the same chemical processes that occur in muscle also occur in liver, kidney and brain cells. Extracts of yeast, the fungus that is commercially important in the making of bread and in brewing, also exhibit similar chemical changes. It would seem likely, therefore, that the breakdown of carbohydrate and its phosphorylation with the subsequent release of energy constitute a metabolic process that is basic to life as a whole and not just to vertebrate muscle. Bio-chemical similarities of this nature are strong evidence for a common origin of life.

CHAPTER EIGHTEEN

The Work of the Kidney

UNLESS a fire is regularly raked to remove ash and to maintain an adequate supply of air it will eventually go out. The waste materials (ash) produced by the burning of the fuel choke up the fire and prevent it from burning. Living cells burn fuel to produce the energy needed for muscle action, replacement of damaged or worn-out tissues and the building of new tissues. This produces waste substances, some of which (e.g. lactic acid) can be broken down further to yield more energy, but others have to be removed from the body in order that the living processes can continue. If waste substances are allowed to accumulate they produce a number of harmful effects and eventually the organism dies.

The removal of waste substances from the body, mainly by the kidneys, is called *excretion*. In man, other forms of excretion include the removal

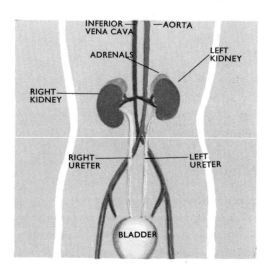

The excretory system in man showing the relationships of the kidneys, their blood supply, the ureters and the bladder.

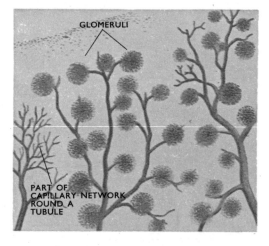

A section of kidney tissue (highly magnified) in which the arteries have been injected with dye showing clearly the knots of capillaries (glomeruli).

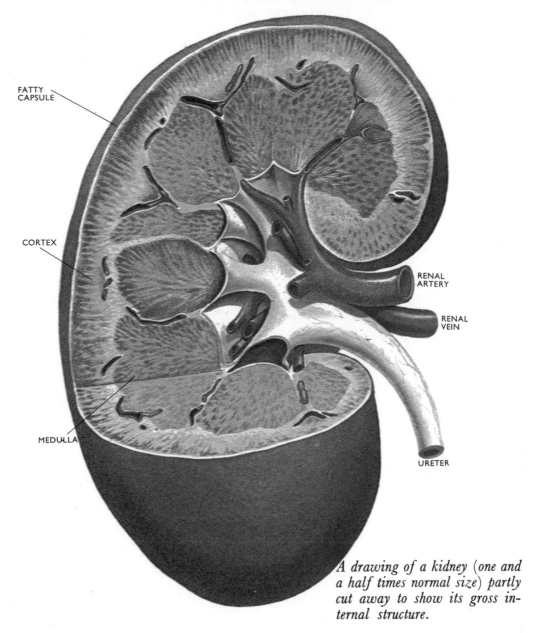

FATTY CAPSULE

CORTEX

MEDULLA

RENAL ARTERY

RENAL VEIN

URETER

A drawing of a kidney (one and a half times normal size) partly cut away to show its gross internal structure.

of carbon dioxide from the lungs when we breathe out, sweating, and the growth of hair and nails. True excretion, however, should be restricted to the breakdown of wastes and their elimination by the kidneys in the urine.

The work of the kidneys is much more than just the removal of waste, however. They play a part in controlling the quantity of water lost to the outside world; they help regulate the pH (i.e. level of acidity or alkalinity) of the blood and the general balance of ions in the blood, and hence in the body fluid as a whole; and lastly they conserve essential substances such as glucose and amino-acids.

When the kidneys fail to function efficiently it is sometimes possible for doctors to employ an artificial kidney which temporarily takes over the work of the patient's kidney and purifies his blood.

The Structure of the Kidneys

In man, the kidneys are paired, bean-shaped organs, one on each side of the backbone, lying under the gut in the 'small-of-the-back'.

A lengthwise section through a kidney shows two main zones: an outer *cortex* and an inner *medulla*. The whole is encased in a protective, fatty *capsule*.

Within the cortex and medulla are masses of tubules. They make up the bulk of the kidney tissue and join up with larger *collecting tubes* that eventually form the main urine-carrying duct or *ureter*. This channels urine from the kidney to the bladder. Each kidney tubule has a rich blood supply: the renal artery and renal

A diagram of a single kidney tubule. Arrows show the direction of blood flow and the flow of urine.

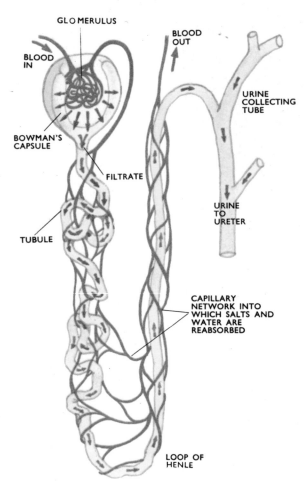

GLOMERULUS

BLOOD IN

BLOOD OUT

BOWMAN'S CAPSULE

URINE COLLECTING TUBE

FILTRATE

URINE TO URETER

TUBULE

CAPILLARY NETWORK INTO WHICH SALTS AND WATER ARE REABSORBED

LOOP OF HENLE

vein (together with the ureter) are prominent vessels entering or leaving the kidney.

The blind end of each kidney tubule lies in the cortex and may be likened to a champagne glass, the walls and stem of which are hollow and one cell thick. The 'bowl' of the tubule is called *Bowman's capsule*. It surrounds an elaborate knot of blood capillaries —tiny branches of the renal artery— called the *glomerulus*. Each Bowman's capsule and glomerulus together form the *Malpighian body*—there are at least a million such structures in a single human kidney!

The hollow stem of the champagne glass is the upper part of the kidney tubule. This descends into the medulla where it narrows before turning upwards and ascending back into the cortex—increasing in diameter again. The thin portion of the tubule is known as the *loop of Henle* and is primarily concerned with the absorption of water. The ascending limb of the tubule joins a collecting duct which joins with others before eventually discharging its urine into the ureter.

In effect each Bowman's capsule is a tiny filter. Blood containing waste substances, proteins, sugars etc., is forced to the kidneys by the pumping action of the heart. Under pressure, a solution is driven out of the capillaries of the glomerulus through the walls of the capsule into its hollow interior. (Materials are supplied to the tissues in a similar way.) The solution in the capsule is blood plasma minus the large (colloidal) molecules. These are too big to pass through the capillary wall.

From the capsule the fluid passes along the tubule. Many of the substances in it are absorbed through the tubule wall into the blood capillaries that envelop this, so that it gradually becomes more concentrated. Organic molecules such as some amino-acids and glucose, some salts and water are absorbed in the descending or *proximal* limb of the tubule, whilst more water and salts are absorbed in the ascending or *distal* limb. Certain poisonous or toxic substances that have been rendered harmless (detoxicated) are released into the urine by the tubules, together with potassium and hydrogen. Measurements of the amounts of various substances present in the blood and in the urine show striking differences. The concentration of the principal waste substance in the urine (urea) is normally seventy times as great as it is in the blood, yet, surprisingly enough, some urea is reabsorbed, since a certain blood concentration is needed. Ninety times more sulphate, nine times more potassium and twenty-five times more uric acid occur in the urine than in the blood. On the other hand no glucose, fatty substances, proteins or bicarbonate ions normally occur in the urine, whereas considerable quantities occur in the blood.

The normal daily output of urine is between two and a half to three pints, yet it is calculated that a total of nearly three hundred pints of fluid is filtered by the kidneys during that time. They not only reabsorb a vast volume each day; they also regu-

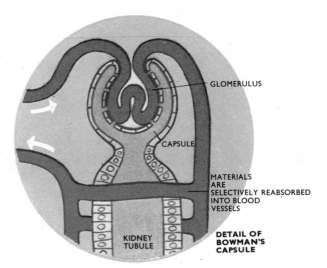

Diagram of Bowman's capsule with glomerulus.

late its content so that the correct levels of essential substances are maintained in the body fluids.

The function of the various parts of the tubule has been analysed by inserting tiny pipettes into them and withdrawing small quantities of the fluid. Differences in the concentrations of substances in the fluid in different parts are strong evidence as to the function of a particular part. The content of the urine varies considerably with the type of diet that a person eats, however. For example, the nitrogen content of the urine is much higher in someone taking a protein-rich diet than in another who is eating starch-rich food, mainly due to the increased production of urea.

CHAPTER NINETEEN

The Artificial Kidney

OBVIOUSLY the artificial kidney cannot hope to match the natural kidney's delicate functioning, its perfect co-ordination with other parts of the body. Nevertheless, introduced in 1945, it has become an important life-saver and an instrument of limitless research.

Its essential component is just a long tube made of a cellophane membrane. Cellophane resembles the walls of blood capillaries in having pores of almost exactly the same size. Consequently, the same types of substance can penetrate both surfaces.

The principle on which the artificial kidney functions – *dialysis* – is also very simple. If two solutions are separated by a porous membrane, molecules and atoms will move to and fro from one solution to another. For any one type of particle, the overall transfer will be towards the solution with least concentration of that particle; the particles will tend to move from one area of high concentration to an area of low concentration.

To remove poisonous waste products such as urea, blood simply has to be circulated in cellophane tubes through a solution in which the concentration of this substance is low. As the movement of each type of atom or

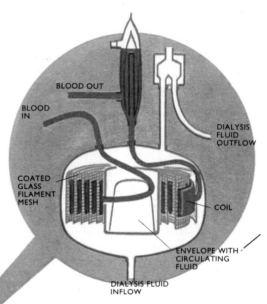

BLOOD OUT

BLOOD IN

DIALYSIS FLUID OUTFLOW

COATED GLASS FILAMENT MESH

COIL

ENVELOPE WITH CIRCULATING FLUID

DIALYSIS FLUID INFLOW

This mini-coil artificial kidney is capable of ultra-filtration. The design is based upon Kolff's disposable coil kidney, first developed in 1956.

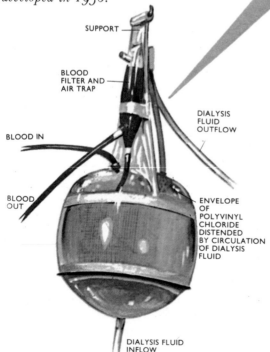

SUPPORT

BLOOD FILTER AND AIR TRAP

DIALYSIS FLUID OUTFLOW

BLOOD IN

BLOOD OUT

ENVELOPE OF POLYVINYL CHLORIDE DISTENDED BY CIRCULATION OF DIALYSIS FLUID

DIALYSIS FLUID INFLOW

molecule is largely independent of the other types, a 'rinsing' fluid can be prepared of right composition not only for removing waste products such as urea but keeping the concentration of other substances at a constant level, and, if necessary, actually adding ingredients.

The earliest type of kidney functions solely by dialysis. The instigator of this machine was Wilhelm Kolff. Blood from a patient with defective kidneys is passed along a cellophane tube wrapped about a rotating drum. The rotation of the drum moves the blood by gravity through a bath filled with rinsing fluid and noxious

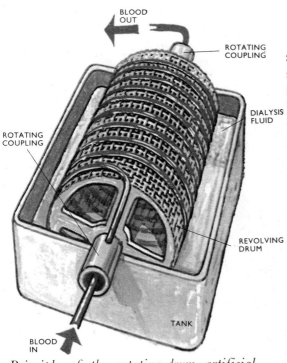

substances are removed without up-setting the balance of other substances. Such artificial kidneys have saved hundreds of lives from uremia (self-poisoning due to a build up of urea in the body) when natural kidneys through shock or disease have failed to function properly.

Of far wider application today are artificial kidneys designed to not only remove wastes by dialysis but also to remove excess body fluid from the blood by *ultrafiltration*. A very common variety is based upon Kolff's *disposable coil kidney* developed in 1956. Here, unlike the rotating drum models, coils of cellophane tubing are supported by fibre-glass screens and wrapped about a central cylinder. The whole unit fits neatly into a container through which rinsing fluid is in continuous circulation. The compression of the cellophane tubes by the screens maintains the pressure of the blood flowing through. Under this pressure, excess

Principle of the rotating-drum artificial kidney. Celluloid tubing is wrapped about the drum; when the drum rotates the blood is moved by gravity through the bath of prepared dialysis fluid. Exchange of ions purifies the blood.

Showing the principle of dialysis – how substances move through pores in a membrane from an area of high to an area of low concentration. By preparing a suitable dialysis fluid components can if necessary be removed from the blood (right).

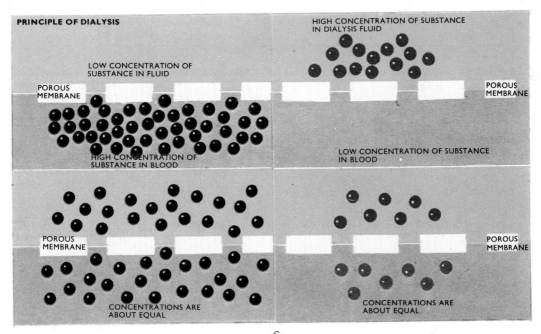

An artificial kidney. Blood from the patient is passed through coils in the large drum-shaped containers where waste substances are extracted. The blood is then returned to the patient's circulatory system.

fluid in the blood flows out through the membrane. A pumping device can be used to boost the pressure of the blood before it passes through the coil.

Other Uses for the Artificial Kidney

Accumulated waste products such as urea can be removed from the body using the artificial kidney. The abnormally high or low concentration of any other ion or compound can also be rectified. All that is needed is a rinsing fluid containing the correct concentration of substances. Thus the artificial kidney provides a standard method for treating barbiturate or salycic poisoning. In this respect the artificial kidney is more efficient than the natural kidney, for the poisons can be completely removed from the blood stream; there is no question of any reabsorption after filtering.

Since the artificial kidney can effectively control the quantities of the various constituents of the blood, it is a simple matter in experiments to change the concentrations of specific substances whilst at the same time keeping other constituents at a constant level. In this way the causes of a number of diseases can be discovered with means of applying remedies.

Keeping the Blood Flowing

When the artificial kidney was developed one immediate difficulty to overcome was how to prevent blood clotting once it was circulating in the cellophane tubes. Originally *hirudin* was used. Hirudin is a substance produced by leeches – the *hirudinea*. These creatures lead a blood-sucking mode of life and the hirudin facilitates their feeding. In order to extract enough of the chemical for an experiment, thousands of leeches were necessary.

Today other anticoagulants, which can be prepared artificially, are available. Most important is *heparin*, discovered in the early 1930's.

The Heart's Rhythm
and the Need for
Respiration

CHAPTER TWENTY

⁓ The Human Heart and Circulation

WHILE working normally we are hardly aware of the heart's rhythmic beat, but after strenuous exercise it beats so much more strongly that we may feel as though it is trying to burst its way out of the body. This is but one instance of the way in which the activities of some parts of the body are continually changing to cope with the varying demands of other tissues. Just as the heartbeat varies so does the blood supply to different parts of the body. When we move, the supply to the muscles is increased, more channels are opened up there to carry the increased supply in order that the tissues can receive greater quantities of fuel and the oxygen needed to burn it. At the same time the supply to the skin and the gut may be cut down.

Thus, though the larger vessels are constantly carrying blood, the extremities of the system may be opened and closed as the situation demands. Even so the diameter of the large vessels can be increased or decreased as the volume of blood flow rises or falls so that all parts of the system are plastic.

We know that most of the substances in the blood are not confined to the system of blood vessels. Oxygen and the products of the digestion of food pass out of the capillaries into the tissues and waste materials etc., pass in. When the muscles are working the extra fuel that they need (glucose) is released into the bloodstream by the liver. The kidneys extract waste matter from the blood so that its composition on entering and leaving that organ is changed. Not only are parts of the vessel system adjustable but also the fluid within them is continually having some materials added to it and others taken away.

The heart beats approximately 70 times per minute and a complete circulation takes approximately twenty-five seconds. The blood is pumped to the tissues under a high pressure. This is the result of the *double circulation*, an arrangement by which blood poor in oxygen, returning to the heart from the tissues, is kept separate from blood rich in oxygen that has returned from the lungs and is about to be pumped round the body again. Oxygenated blood, therefore, has to pass only through the capillary system in the tissues on its way round the body.

The human heart is a muscular four-chambered sac situated underneath the breastbone and between the lungs. It is divided vertically into right and left halves and each half has two compartments. The top compartments are called *auricles* (or atria) and the lower ones *ventricles*. The latter have thick muscular walls by whose contraction blood is forced out of the heart to the lungs and to the body.

Blood from the head and body enters the right *auricle* through large veins. A valve opens to allow blood into the right *ventricle* which contracts forcing blood out through a large vessel, the *pulmonary artery*, that has a right and a left branch. Each

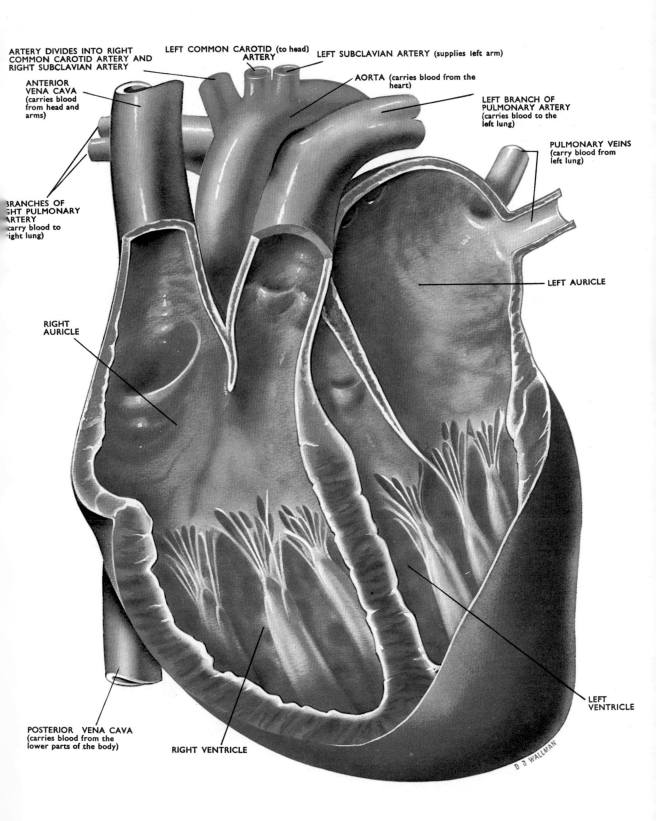

ARTERY DIVIDES INTO RIGHT COMMON CAROTID ARTERY AND RIGHT SUBCLAVIAN ARTERY

LEFT COMMON CAROTID (to head) ARTERY

LEFT SUBCLAVIAN ARTERY (supplies left arm)

ANTERIOR VENA CAVA (carries blood from head and arms)

AORTA (carries blood from the heart)

LEFT BRANCH OF PULMONARY ARTERY (carries blood to the left lung)

PULMONARY VEINS (carry blood from left lung)

BRANCHES OF RIGHT PULMONARY ARTERY (carry blood to right lung)

LEFT AURICLE

RIGHT AURICLE

POSTERIOR VENA CAVA (carries blood from the lower parts of the body)

RIGHT VENTRICLE

LEFT VENTRICLE

D J WALLMAN

An enlarged view of the human heart from the front, cut away to show its structure.

71

The Heart Cycle

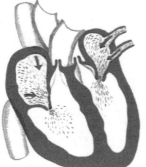

1. *Between heartbeats (i.e. when the heart is relaxed) both auricles are filled with blood. A little may enter the ventricles.*

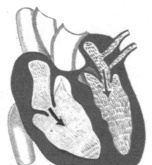

2. *The valve between each auricle and ventricle opens as the auricles contract and the ventricles are filled with blood.*

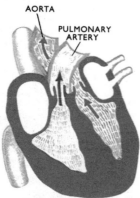

3. *The ventricles contract, forcing blood out of the heart through the valves in the aorta and pulmonary artery.*

supplies a lung in which it splits into a branching mass of capillaries. The blood collects a new supply of oxygen in the lungs and returns to the heart through the *pulmonary veins* which enter the left auricle. A valve opens to allow blood into the left ventricle, which contracts forcing the blood, now rich in oxygen, round the body. Both auricles contract more or less together, as do the two ventricles, so that blood is forced to the lungs and to the body at the same time, but at all times blood rich in oxygen (*i.e.* returning from the lung) is separated from blood poor in oxygen (*i.e.* returning from the body).

Vessels that carry blood away from the heart are called *arteries*. These branch into smaller vessels called *arterioles* which break up in the tissues into *capillaries* – channels whose walls are only one cell thick. Because the capillaries branch so many times in the tissues and because they have thin walls, substances in the blood are brought into close contact with the

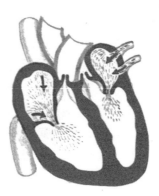

4. *The heart relaxes once more. The auricles fill with blood and the cycle is ready to start again.*

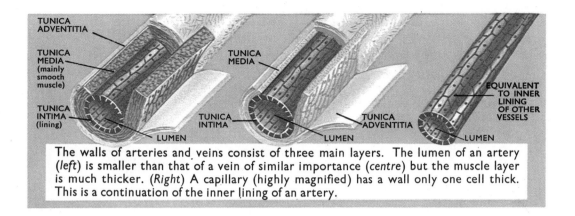

The walls of arteries and veins consist of three main layers. The lumen of an artery (*left*) is smaller than that of a vein of similar importance (*centre*) but the muscle layer is much thicker. (*Right*) A capillary (highly magnified) has a wall only one cell thick. This is a continuation of the inner lining of an artery.

cells and materials can pass easily between them. The capillaries join up again to form *venules* which come together to form *veins* through which blood flows back to the heart. This blood is usually deoxygenated, though in the case of the pulmonary veins the blood is rich in oxygen.

The pressure at which the heart forces blood through the arteries gets smaller and smaller as the arteries branch and their diameters decrease. It is only about one tenth of its original value by the time the blood emerges from the capillary network into the veins. This venous blood pressure is not sufficient to force blood back to the heart. How then does blood pass from the veins to the heart? The sucking action of the heart is partly responsible, but this too is not strong enough on its own. The veins themselves are able to contract and they help to force the blood into the heart. They have valves which prevent the blood from flowing away from the heart (the valves of the veins on the inside of the forearm can be seen as swellings by tying a bandage round the arm just above the elbow). Their walls are thin and not so muscular

as those of arteries but the lumen or bore is greater. The contraction of the muscles also massages the blood along towards the heart.

Heart muscle is striped in appearance but, unlike striated (voluntary) muscle fibres, its fibres are branched. The branching and interlacing of neighbouring fibres is ideally suited to that of an elastic bag-shaped organ which is repeatedly contracting and expanding. It is essential that the heartbeat should be smooth and that the beat of different parts should be co-ordinated. Though heart muscle beats of its own accord (*i.e.* without receiving nerve signals) the frequency of the beat is controlled by nerves. Two sets of nerve fibres supply the heart, one parasympathetic in the *vagus nerve*, the other sympathetic. The heartbeat actually originates in one small area (the *sinu-auricular node*) in the wall of the right auricle. It consists of special muscle fibres and nerve fibres from the vagus nerve and a sympathetic nerve and is the so-called *pacemaker* of the heart. Signals from the vagus nerve slow the heartbeat, whilst sympathetic signals increase it. Contraction of the heart muscle spreads rapidly (one metre per second) over the auricles so that they beat more or less together. Another special area (the *auriculo-ventricular*

node) takes up the beat of the auricles and passes signals along a band of tissue – the *bundle of His* – which branches to both ventricles. These

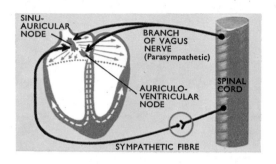

A diagram showing the nerve supply of the heart and the conducting system.

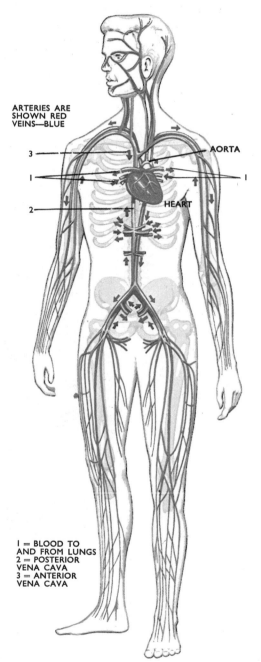

ARTERIES ARE
SHOWN RED
VEINS—BLUE

AORTA

HEART

1 = BLOOD TO
AND FROM LUNGS
2 = POSTERIOR
VENA CAVA
3 = ANTERIOR
VENA CAVA

The human blood system.

beat almost together therefore. The wave of contraction spreads over them at one tenth of a metre per second. Heart muscle has a long period of relaxation after a contraction during which it will not contract again. This ensures that another heartbeat will not start before the last one has finished. The period of contraction is called *systole* and relaxation *diastole*. Systole takes four tenths of a second (the auricle one tenth of a second, the ventricle three tenths of a second) and diastole lasts for a further four tenths of a second, a total of eight tenths of a second. In times of stress the heartbeat may increase considerably. Various factors such as emotion, the rate of breathing, temperature, exercise, the volume of blood flowing into the right auricle and out of the aorta and the quantities of oxygen and carbon dioxide in the blood can affect the heartbeat.

CHAPTER TWENTY-ONE

Body Fluids

A FLOWER placed in an empty vase quickly wilts and dies. Its tissues dry up because they lack water. In the same way the body cells would shrivel up and die if they were not bathed by fluid. This fluid, the *intercellular* or *interstitial fluid*, contains all the materials that the cells need for their continued activity, and the waste materials that this activity produces are removed via the same fluid.

The interstitial fluid is in close contact with the blood system. It receives a supply of fuel, oxygen and other substances from the blood – the latter having obtained these from the digestive system, lungs and the glands. Waste materials pass from it in the reverse direction, and are removed from the blood mainly by the lungs and kidneys. (The *lymphatic system* provides another route by which material is returned from the tissues to the blood).

The body contains approximately nine pints of blood, just over half of which consists of the fluid part (*plasma*). But this is only a small part of the fluid within the body. The plasma and the interstitial fluid together make up a total of between eighty and ninety pints! The composition of the body fluids varies between different parts of the body and from time to time with the activity of the tissue with which it is in contact. For example, the quantities of waste materials in the fluid bathing muscle cells will increase during vigorous exercise. At the same time the spleen releases more red corpuscles into the blood thus increasing its oxygen-carrying capacity.

One striking fact is the difference between the composition of the fluid outside the cells and that inside (the *intercellular fluid*). In muscle, for

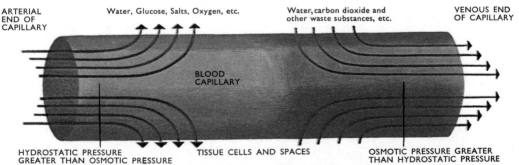

ARTERIAL END OF CAPILLARY   Water, Glucose, Salts, Oxygen, etc.   Water, carbon dioxide and other waste substances, etc.   VENOUS END OF CAPILLARY

BLOOD CAPILLARY

HYDROSTATIC PRESSURE GREATER THAN OSMOTIC PRESSURE   TISSUE CELLS AND SPACES   OSMOTIC PRESSURE GREATER THAN HYDROSTATIC PRESSURE

A diagram showing the circulation of fluid between the blood capillaries and the cells and spaces of the tissues. Water and dissolved substances other than proteins are driven out of the capillary at the arterial end because the pressure due to the heartbeat (hydrostatic pressure) is greater than the osmotic pressure. Waste materials, some salts and water are 'sucked' into the capillary at its venous end because the osmotic pressure is greater than the hydrostatic pressure.

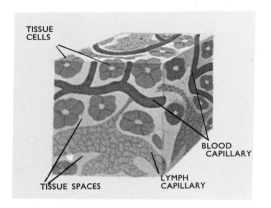

A block of tissue showing diagrammatically the relationship of the tissue cells, tissue spaces, lymph capillaries and blood capillaries.

example, the interstitial fluid is rich in sodium, chloride and bicarbonate ions but has relatively little potassium, calcium or magnesium. The intracellular fluid, on the other hand, is rich in potassium, magnesium, phosphate and protein. Nerve cells too are rich in potassium and protein but contain very little chloride or sodium, though the fluid round nerves is rich in sodium and chloride but poor in potassium and protein. These differences in concentration are particularly important in the functioning of nerves.

Even when fluid is retained within fairly well-defined regions of the body it is not entirely distinct from fluid elsewhere for there is a constant exchange of materials between different regions.

Water, glucose, oxygen, amino acids and salts continually pass from the blood to the tissues through the capillary walls. Waste materials and water pass from the tissues into the blood. The lymph (see page 78) is slowly but constantly returned to the blood. Great changes in the blood composition occur as it passes through the kidneys. However, variations in the composition of the body fluid are so complicated that it is impractical to consider it as a whole. The following divisions will be discussed here; blood and the lymph.

> *The structure of the blood is described in chapter one, its role in respiration in chapter twenty-six.*

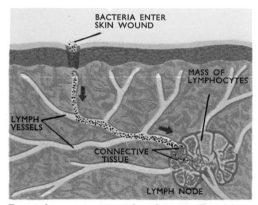

Bacteria may enter the tissues through a skin wound. They enter the lymph vessels and are carried to the lymph nodes where many are destroyed by phagocytes.

A series of drawings showing a phagocyte engulfing and destroying a bacterium, a process called phagocytosis.

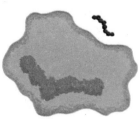

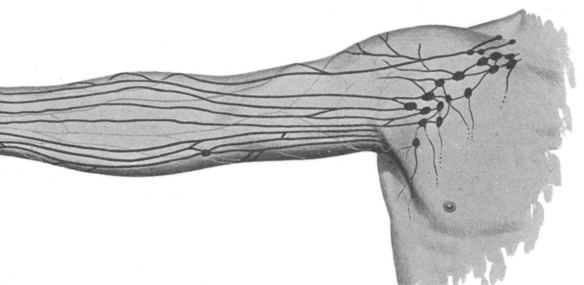

A diagram showing the main lymph vessels and lymph nodes of a human arm.

The Blood

The blood *plasma* contains nearly seven per cent of protein, about one per cent of inorganic salts and small amounts of organic substances such as glucose, amino acids, fat, enzymes, hormones, antibodies and urea (the main waste material formed by the breakdown of protein).

The blood is pumped at a high pressure to the tissues. This pressure is greater than that produced by the large molecules of the blood proteins (the *blood osmotic pressure*). Water, salts, glucose and other substances with molecules small enough to pass through the capillary walls are driven *out* of the capillaries to the fluid round the tissues. The blood pressure produced by the heartbeat drops as it passes further through the capillary network until it becomes less than the osmotic pressure. Thus water and waste materials are sucked back into the capillaries. In this way the cells are nourished and relieved of waste materials.

Substances with small molecules probably seep (diffuse) through the walls of the capillaries because of concentration differences between the plasma and the tissue fluids.

The greater part of the plasma is water. Consequently many of the activities of the blood are directly related to the properties of water. Because water loses and gains heat more slowly than any other substance the blood can transport heat from one part of the body to another. Also since the body as a whole contains so much water its temperature will not

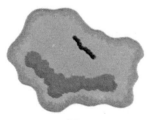

be subject to rapid ups and downs. The conditions under which the tissues work are, therefore, more constant. More substances will dissolve in water than in any other solvent, so the blood can transport chemicals from one part of the body to another.

An additional important function of the blood is its role in the body's protective mechanisms against infection. Many of the white cells (*phagocytes*) are able to engulf and destroy bacteria. The harmful substances (*toxins*) that these bacteria produce are also rendered harmless by substances (*antibodies*) produced by the white blood cells and in certain of the body organs.

The Lymphatic System

A special set of vessels, the *lymphatic system*, returns fluid (*lymph*) from the

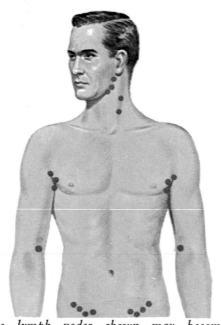

The lymph nodes shown may become swollen and painful. This is a sign that the phagocytes are actively engaged in defending the body against harmful bacteria.

tissues to the heart. Its vessels reach nearly all parts of the body. The lymph capillaries are blind tubes – a little larger in diameter than the blood capillaries. They are in close contact with the tissue cells or the spaces round them. Although the tubes are blind, molecules of all shapes and sizes (even bacteria) can squeeze through the walls between cells. The smaller vessels join up to form larger ones in much the same way as veins. At intervals along the lymph channels are swellings – the *lymph nodes*. These are essentially networks of connective tissue that contain phagocytes and also other white blood cells called *lymphocytes*. The lymph nodes are particularly important at times of infection when the phagocytes actively consume bacteria. They are the 'swollen glands' that we feel in the armpits from an infected finger or in the neck from a bad tooth. Nodes near the lungs of city dwellers may become blackened by soot and other particles. Thus a major function of the lymphatic system is as a filter for bacteria and other foreign particles.

The lymphatic system is also concerned with maintaining the fluid balance of the tissue cells and the spaces round them. When channels become blocked by disease the affected part may swell considerably, a condition called *oedema*. The lymph vessels (*lacteals*) of the intestine transport fat away from the intestine.

The chemical composition of lymph is very similar to that of the blood plasma except that it contains very little protein. It is moved very slowly through the lymph vessels as a result of body movements. Valves similar to those of veins prevent its backward flow.

CHAPTER TWENTY-TWO

Haemoglobin

ALL animals require a supply of oxygen for the process of respiration whereby food materials are oxidized with the liberation of energy. The blood system of man is really a transport system. One of its functions is to carry oxygen from the respiratory organs (lungs) to the rest of the body.

The solubility of oxygen is not high and although there is a very large surface for absorbing it, it will not dissolve in the blood in quantities sufficient for the needs of active tissues. This is where the *blood pigments* come into play. The best known of these is *haemoglobin*, the red pigment of vertebrate blood and of some other animals (e.g. earthworms).

Blood pigments are substances with a high affinity for oxygen when the latter is plentiful but which release it again in oxygen-deficient surroundings. Thus, when the blood flows through the lungs, the pigment combines with oxygen. On its journey round the body, the blood meets oxygen-deficient tissues which are slightly acidic because of the carbon dioxide that has been formed during respiration. The oxygen is then released by the pigment and made available for further respiration.

Haemoglobin is mainly carried in the red corpuscles of the blood in vertebrates. It makes up about 32% of the dry weight of the corpuscles. There are two basic parts to the haemoglobin molecule; *haem*, containing the iron, and *globin*, which is a complicated protein. Globin makes up about 96% of the haemoglobin. The formula of haem is now known to be $C_{34}H_{32}O_4N_4FeOH$, although it is not obtained in this form. Hydrolysis of haemoglobin with hydrochloric acid produces *haemin* (hemin) in which a chlorine atom has replaced the hy-

Iron deficiency in the body leads to reduction of haemoglobin content. This is measured by comparing a sample of blood taken from the ear or finger with a standard chart. The redder the colour the greater the haemoglobin content.

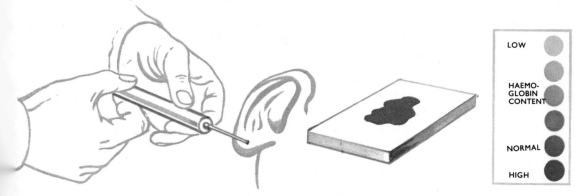

LOW

HAEMO-
GLOBIN
CONTENT

NORMAL

HIGH

Dr J. C. Kendrew (left) and Dr Max Perutz shared a Nobel prize in 1962 for their work in determining the structure of haemoglobin and the related myoglobin. Here, they are discussing a model constructed to show molecular structures.

droxyl (OH) group. Haem is chemically related to chlorophyll and other naturally occurring pigments. Although it is the smaller part of the molecule, the haem group is the functional part as far as oxygen-carrying is concerned. The constituent amino-acids of globin give the haemoglobin molecule as a whole a very high molecular weight.

After its journey round the body, the blood is returned to the lungs. The concentration of oxygen is lower inside the blood vessels of the lungs than outside, and oxygen passes into the blood stream and into combination with the haemoglobin, forming *oxyhaemoglobin*. The latter is bright red and accounts for the difference in colour between oxygenated (arterial) blood and venous blood which is a dark reddish brown. One gram of haemoglobin combines (under standard atmospheric conditions) with

1.35 c.c. of oxygen, corresponding to one atom of oxygen for each one of iron:

Haemoglobin + oxygen = oxyhaemoglobin.

The reaction is reversible, the direction depending upon the concentration of oxygen around, and upon the acidity of the surroundings. Oxygen is readily released in the body where the concentration is low and the acidity high.

Carbon monoxide also forms a compound with haemoglobin. It is called *carboxyhaemoglobin* and is again, bright red. Carboxyhaemoglobin is much more stable than oxyhaemoglobin and does not readily break down. The pigment is thus permanently prevented from carrying oxygen again. This explains the extremely poisonous nature of carbon monoxide.

CHAPTER TWENTY-THREE

Blood Groups

AT the present time blood transfusions are everyday things in connection with accidents and operations. A transfusion involves the introduction of blood – given by a *donor* – into the blood stream of the patient. Blood consists of a liquid part – the *plasma* or *serum* – which contains various dissolved substances, and a solid part – the red and white corpuscles. The red ones are important as oxygen carriers. The normal purpose of a transfusion is to increase the volume and oxygen-carrying capacity of the patient's blood stream after prolonged bleeding (*haemorrhage*). However, the

patient cannot be given blood from any donor. It must be of the right *group*.

The work of Landsteiner and others at the beginning of this century showed that blood varies according to the presence or absence of two substances in the red corpuscles. These substances are called *agglutinogens* or *antigens* and are complicated proteins. For simplicity, they are referred to as A and B. According to the presence or absence of these substances, four groups are recognised: Group A has substance A only in the corpuscles; Group B has substance B; Group AB contains both; and Group O has neither. This scheme of classification is called the ABO system. When the blood of these groups is mixed a reaction occurs – the corpuscles clump together (agglutinate). Landsteiner showed that this feature is caused by two other substances which occur in the plasma. These are called *agglutinins* or *antibodies*. One of them reacts with agglutinogen A and the other with B. They are therefore termed *anti-A* and *anti-B* respectively. Obviously the antibodies cannot exist naturally with their respective antigens.

The discovery of these blood groups was fundamental to the development of blood transfusion. The corpuscles of the donated blood must be *compatible* with the serum of the patient (*i.e.* there must be no agglutination). The serum of the donated blood is diluted in the patient's body and this does little harm to the patient's red

Group	Antigens	Antibodies
A	A	anti-B
B	B	anti-A
AB	A + B	none
O	none	anti-A + anti-B

Donors	Recipients			
	O	A	B	AB
A	X	C	X	C
B	X	X	C	C
AB	X	X	X	C
O	C	C	C	C

C denotes satisfactory mixing.
X denotes agglutination of the donor's corpuscles.

corpuscles. It is the *patient's serum* and *donor's corpuscles* which must not react.

From the table we see that blood Group O – with no antigens in the

Blood is tested for its group on a white tile by skilled technicians. Drops of anti-A and anti-B serum are placed on the tile and a drop of the specimen blood added. Agglutina-

	KNOWN SAMPLES ARE PLACED IN THESE COLUMNS			
	SERUM		CORPUSCLES	
	ANTI-A	ANTI-B	A	B
THE UNKNOWN BLOOD IS PLACED IN EACH DROP UNKNOWN IS GROUP O				
UNKNOWN IS GROUP AB				
UNKNOWN IS GROUP B				
UNKNOWN IS				

Grouping **tests** are performed on white tiles like this. Known **serum** and corpuscles are used to group unknown blood.

corpuscles – can be given safely to a patient of any group. Group O is thus called the *universal donor*. Similarly, group AB – with no antibodies – will not agglutinate any corpuscles and is therefore known as the *universal recipient*. Although these possibilities are useful in an emergency, it is usual to transfuse blood of the same group.

tion in both means that the specimen is AB; agglutination with anti-A means Group A; with anti-B, Group B; and no agglutination indicates Group O. The test may also be done in a test tube. A second check is done with known corpuscles – Groups A and B – and in all, three checks are made on the ABO groupings of donated blood.

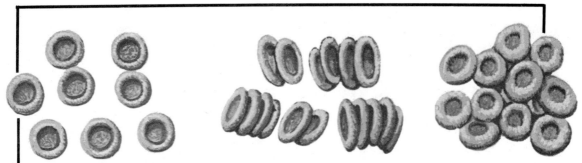

(left) Normal red corpuscles. *(centre)* Naturally clotted corpuscles which form scabs and *(right)* agglutinated corpuscles.

Blood keeps in good condition for about three weeks at 4°C. Any blood not used within this period is used as a source of dried plasma. This keeps indefinitely and can be reconstituted when needed by adding distilled water. Plasma is useful for keeping the volume of blood at its normal level until whole blood is available and in certain types of accident, such as burns, where plasma is lost but not corpuscles. Plasma, which is a mixture from all groups, can be given with safety.

Although the ABO grouping is the most important, it is by no means the only grouping. Many other substances are known which occur in the corpuscles but no natural antibodies are known and it is rare for them to be formed in the patient's blood after transfusions. These other groups are not therefore very important for the purposes of blood transfusion. They do have uses, however, especially in medico-legal work. For example, bloodstains of group M could not have come from a man with group N blood (the MN system being a fairly widely used one). But just because the stains are group M they need not necessarily be those of *a particular man* with group M blood. The blood group tests are merely *exclusive*. Disputed paternity cases can frequently be settled by using blood groups as they are inherited according to definite patterns.

CHAPTER TWENTY-FOUR

The Rhesus Factor

THE rhesus factor – so called because it was first discovered in rhesus monkeys – is a substance (more correctly a group of substances) present in the red blood cells of the majority of people (the actual percentage varies from region to region). These people are said to be rhesus *positive* (Rh +) while those who lack the factor are said to be rhesus *negative* (Rh –). The rhesus grouping is quite independent of th ABO grouping.

If Rh+ is transfused into an Rh– person it is treated rather like a germ would be treated. The Rh– blood produces chemical substances (*antibodies*) that destroy the rhesus factor. The formation of antibodies is slow and a first transfusion of Rh+ blood into an Rh— person may have no harmful effect. Antibodies are almost certain to be produced in the Rh— person, however, and these antibodies will remain in the blood – just like the antibodies produced by vaccination. If a further transfusion of positive blood is given it will be partly destroyed by the antibodies. If the antibody concentration builds up, any later transfusion of Rh+ blood will be completely destroyed – sometimes with fatal results. It is therefore vital that Rh— people should receive only Rh— blood.

The rhesus factor is especially important in expectant mothers who should always be tested for rhesus grouping. The rhesus factor is controlled by genes from both parents and it is common for an Rh— woman to have an Rh+ baby. In rare instances some of the baby's blood may get into the mother's blood-stream and trigger off the production of antibodies. These antibodies are very unlikely to affect the first baby but they remain in the mother's blood-stream and would al-most certainly affect a subsequent Rh+ baby. If the mother had previously received a transfusion of Rh+ blood, however, a first Rh+ baby would be affected.

Rhesus antibodies are dissolved in the blood plasma and can pass across into the unborn baby. If the baby's blood is rhesus positive, the antibodies will attach themselves to the red corpuscles and begin to destroy them. This results in the condition called *haemolytic anaemia* in the new-born baby. The blood cells are destroyed almost as soon as they are formed. This condition was formerly incurable but modern techniques of blood transfusion have overcome it.

If blood tests on the mother show that Rh antibodies are present in high concentration, there is a strong likelihood of the baby's being seriously affected. Transfusion apparatus is made ready and, if the baby is anaemic, its blood is completely replaced by transfusion with Rh— negative blood. In due course the baby's body will produce its own blood (Rh+) and the Rh— blood will be broken down naturally before it has time to produce antibodies.

CHAPTER TWENTY-FIVE

Breathing in Man

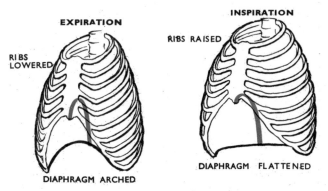

The position of the ribs and diaphragm at inspiration (right) and expiration (left).

EACH lung is like a tree, the branches of which are hollow and represent the bronchi and bronchioles; each cluster of leaves represents a cluster of tiny hollow air sacs – the *alveoli*. But each respiratory tree is enclosed in a layer of tissue, the *pleura*, and all parts of it have a rich blood supply. The alveoli and the bronchioles have elastic fibres in their walls. The elastic fibres give, so allowing the lungs to expand at inspiration (breathing in) and when they contract (*i.e.* shorten) during expiration (breathing out) air is forced out of the lungs. Expiration is thus largely accomplished by the action of the elastic fibres for little muscular effort is involved. A person suffering an attack of asthma has difficulty in breathing out because the smooth muscle in the bronchioles contracts thus reducing the expansion of the lungs, and hence the stretching of the elastic fibres, at inspiration. The force exerted by the shortening of the elastic fibres is therefore less than normal at expiration.

The lungs are situated in a cavity, the *pleural cavity*, which is surrounded below by the *diaphragm*, a muscular sheet, and on the other sides by the ribs. The ribs are provided with muscles, the *intercostals*, and during breathing are held by the *scalene* muscles from above and the *abdominal muscles* from below. The diaphragm is domed upwards underneath the ribs. At inspiration it becomes flattened (and so is lowered) when its muscles contract. This, with the action of the intercostals pulling the ribs out, enlarges the pleural cavity and reduces the pressure on the lungs. Atmospheric pressure therefore forces air

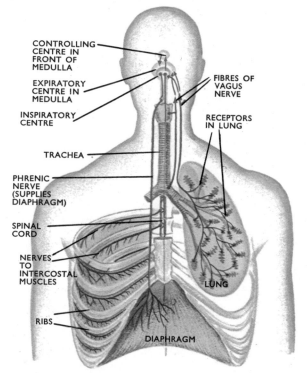

A diagram showing some of the nerves to and from structures involved in respiration.

into the lungs. During expiration the intercostals and diaphragm muscles relax and the shortening of the elastic fibres in the lung tissue, together with the pull of the abdominal muscles and another set between the ribs and breastbone, forces air out of the lungs.

Breathing can, of course, be controlled voluntarily but normally it is automatic. A region of the medulla – the *respiratory centre* – sends signals rhythmically in nerves to the intercostal muscles and the muscles of the diaphragm causing them to contract rhythmically. As the lungs are ex-

panded at each inspiration nerve endings attached to muscle cells (receptors) in the lung tubes are stimulated and signals pass from them along nerve fibres to the respiratory centre.

Experiments indicate that the respiratory centre has two main regions, one that produces inspiration and a second that works against it to produce expiration. They are known as the *inspiratory* and *expiratory centres*. As a further complication there is a region in front of the medulla that plays some part in controlling the rhythm of respiration, for when the nerve tracts in front of the medulla

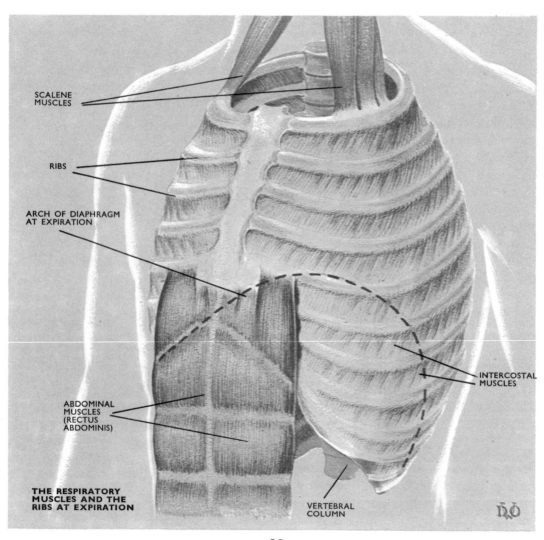

SCALENE
MUSCLES

RIBS

ARCH OF DIAPHRAGM
AT EXPIRATION

INTERCOSTAL
MUSCLES

ABDOMINAL
MUSCLES
(RECTUS
ABDOMINIS)

THE RESPIRATORY
MUSCLES AND THE
RIBS AT EXPIRATION

VERTEBRAL
COLUMN

are cut the rhythm is destroyed. Probably then this region receives signals rhythmically from the inspiratory centre and at the same time signals from the latter pass to the intercostal muscles, the diaphragm and the expiratory centre. The combined influence of the region in front of the medulla, the expiratory centre and signals from the receptors in the lungs over-rules the inspiratory centre and produces expiration.

Breathing is concerned only with ventilating the lungs so that adequate oxygen supplies are inhaled and so that carbon dioxide is exhaled. But the blood system transfers oxygen to, and carbon dioxide away from, the tissues. It is not surprising, therefore, that there are links between the respiratory centre and centres in the brain that control the circulation. The respiratory centre itself is extremely sensitive to the amount of carbon dioxide in the blood and if this amount rises then the rate of breathing will increase. Receptors in the aortic and carotid arches are sensitive to the amount of carbon dioxide and oxygen in the blood.

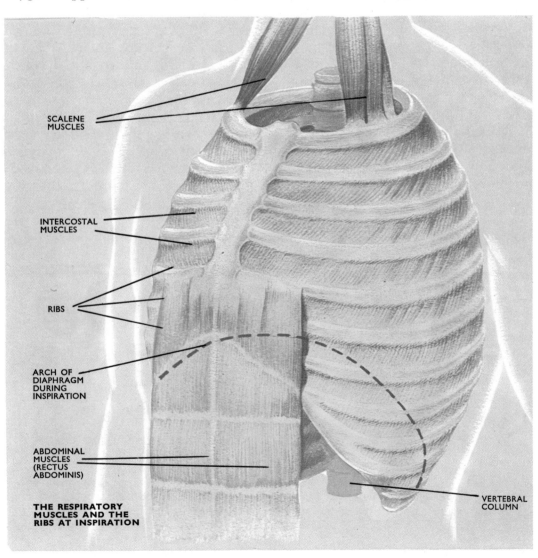

SCALENE
MUSCLES

INTERCOSTAL
MUSCLES

RIBS

ARCH OF
DIAPHRAGM
DURING
INSPIRATION

ABDOMINAL
MUSCLES
(RECTUS
ABDOMINIS)

VERTEBRAL
COLUMN

**THE RESPIRATORY
MUSCLES AND THE
RIBS AT INSPIRATION**

CHAPTER TWENTY-SIX

Respiration

GROWTH and movement, in fact *all* living processes, require energy. This is obtained by oxidation of food materials within the body tissues. In all animals and in the majority of plants the process depends on free oxygen absorbed from the surroundings. The absorption of oxygen, its transport to the tissues, and the oxidation reactions are all classed as respiratory activities, but the term 'respiration' is normally confined to the chemical reactions within the cells.

The essential features of respiratory organs are: a large moist surface area, very thin walls, and a good blood supply. Lungs are internal chambers with no continuous air-flow. They have to be filled and emptied by breathing movements. Each lung is made up of thousands of tiny air-sacs (alveoli) which link together and lead to the bronchi. The alveoli are lined with a thin layer of mucus and on the outside are covered with a network of fine blood capillaries. When air is breathed out, the lung is not completely emptied. A good deal of residual air remains in the alveoli. Oxygen from fresh air breathed in has to diffuse through this residual air and through the mucus before reaching the thin wall of the alveolus. To overcome this disadvantage the total surface is very large.

Oxygen is in solution when it reaches the respiratory surface. The blood arriving here is low in oxygen content and thus the oxygen outside passes in solution through the thin

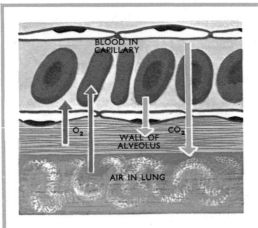
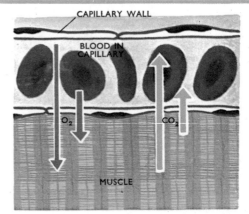

The red blood corpuscles are disc-shaped in man. In the lung capillaries the corpuscles accept oxygen and become bright red. Upon releasing the oxygen in the tissues (*right*) the corpuscles revert to the duller colour of haemoglobin.

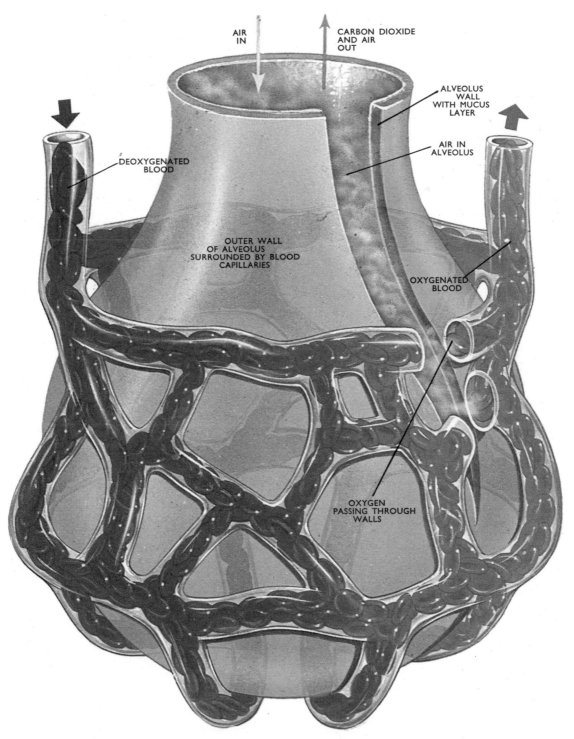

AIR
IN

CARBON DIOXIDE
AND AIR
OUT

ALVEOLUS
WALL
WITH MUCUS
LAYER

DEOXYGENATED
BLOOD

AIR IN
ALVEOLUS

OUTER WALL
OF ALVEOLUS
SURROUNDED BY BLOOD
CAPILLARIES

OXYGENATED
BLOOD

OXYGEN
PASSING THROUGH
WALLS

An alveolus, highly magnified to show its blood supply.

89

walls and into the blood which transports it to the tissues. Only a very small amount of the oxygen is carried as a simple solution in the blood; most of it combines with haemoglobin in the blood. In the body the tissues are low in oxygen content so that the oxygen released passes through the fine capillary walls and into the cells where the chemical reactions take place. These reactions are very complicated and involve numerous enzymes and intermediate stages. The net result, however, can be shown as:

food + oxygen = carbon dioxide + water + energy

This equation holds good for both plants and animals. Glucose is a commonly used food material. Its oxidation can be shown chemically as follows:

$$C_6H_{12}O_6 + 6O_2 = 6CO_2 + 6H_2O + energy$$
(glucose) (oxygen) (carbon dioxide) (water)

Most of the carbon dioxide released is removed by the blood stream. Some is carried in solution and some in combination with blood proteins, but by far the largest amount is carried in the form of bicarbonate ions. In the blood capillaries of the tissues carbon dioxide and water combine to form carbonic acid:

$$CO_2 + H_2O \rightleftharpoons H_2CO_3$$

This then breaks down into ions:

$$H_2CO_3 \rightleftharpoons H+ + HCO_3-.$$

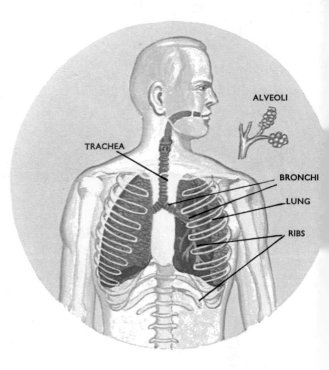

The lungs of man, situated inside the rib cage, communicate with the exterior by way of the bronchi and trachea.

At the respiratory surface the blood becomes more acid (due to the formation of oxyhaemoglobin) and the bicarbonates are broken down, releasing carbon dioxide which passes through the respiratory surface and out to the surroundings.

The Glands

CHAPTER TWENTY-SEVEN

Glands that Produce Hormones

MANY cells in the body are able to produce and release fluid. When this is the main activity of a cell it is called a *gland* cell. A gland is made up of a number of these gland cells, which may be held together by connecting cells (connective tissue). It is usually provided with blood vessels and nerves.

There are two main types of glands: those without ducts, the *ductless* or *endocrine* glands, and those with ducts called *exocrine* glands. Endocrine glands release the fluid they produce either directly into the blood-stream, which carries it to the site of action, or it may be stored and released into the blood-stream at a later date. Exocrine glands release their fluid into a duct which carries it to the site of action or out of the body. Their action is usually fairly local, that is, close to the gland and in one place. In contrast, the fluids released by endocrine glands usually act on a distant part or they may affect the whole body.

Exocrine glands include the *sweat* glands, *salivary* glands and the glands of the *intestine* that produce the digestive enzymes. Examples of endocrine glands are the *pituitary*, *adrenals*, *thyroid*, *parathyroids*, and the *ovaries* and *testes*. The *liver* and the *pancreas* are exocrine as well as endocrine glands. The pancreas, for example, produces *pancreatic juice*, which is released through the pancreatic duct to the intestine, and *insulin* which is released into the blood.

The secretion produced by an endocrine gland is called a *hormone*. It is a chemical-signalling substance carried round the body by the blood-stream. Hormones act as chemical messengers, stimulating some distant part to action. The advantage of these chemical signals is that they quickly reach *all* parts of the body, whereas the signals in nerve fibres reach only certain parts. They work somewhat like the unpleasant smells released into the air system of a coal-mine as a warning of danger. This is much quicker than telephoning each part of the mine in turn.

In any signalling system a signal should produce a particular response, and, under normal circumstances, a hormone acts on a part of the body in the same way each time. *Adrenalin*, a hormone produced by the adrenal gland, causes, among other effects, increased heartbeat when a person is frightened and thus prepares him for action. *Insulin*, produced by the pancreas, has an effect on the amount of glucose in the blood. If the quantity of this sugar in the blood rises, the production of insulin by the pancreas is stepped up to bring the sugar level down to its normal level.

Some hormones (e.g. *thyroxin* produced by the thyroid gland) are thought to alter the actions of enzymes in the cell, whilst others (e.g. *insulin*) are thought to affect the membrane (cell wall) surrounding a cell so that the rates at which substances pass in and out of the cell are changed. Some hormones, for example those produced by the thyroid, appear to have an effect on many different kinds of cells, but others are more *specific* in their action —that is, they affect certain organs only.

It is not really known how hormones act, however. Why one hormone should act on one organ only and another on practically all cells in the body remains to be explained. There is obviously a great deal still to be learned about the chemistry of living cells.

However, the actions of hormones may be placed into three main groups. Firstly, because they are distributed in the blood-stream to all parts of the body, the body can act as one unit in response to a change in the surrounding conditions or in an internal part. In this respect the action of adrenalin has been mentioned. This facet of their action — co-ordination — is closely linked with the co-ordinating activities of the nervous system. Secondly, they control conditions within the animal, ensuring that a '*steady state*' is maintained. Thirdly, hormones play an essential part in controlling growth and development.

Once an organ is suspected of having an endocrine function, many experiments with animals are required to fully prove that it is an endocrine gland. Several techniques should be used. These include removal of a gland; this should produce certain deficiency symptoms. The effects of the removal on other parts—such as structural changes, defects in the workings of an organ and so on—are noted. Having removed an organ, extracts are prepared from it and injected into the animal. This should mean that none of the symptoms noted

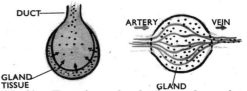

(*Left*) *Exocrine glands have ducts into which their fluid is released.* (*Right*) *Endocrine glands have no ducts; their hormones are released into the bloodstream.*

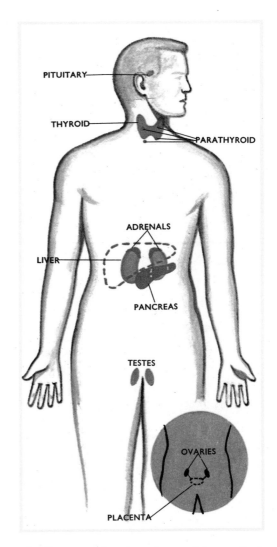

A diagram showing the positions of the main endocrine glands.

93

by merely removing the organ develop. For example, removal of the thyroid slows down growth in young animals. In adults, the working of the body as a whole is slowed down, producing a sluggish individual with marked changes in appearance. The gonads, pituitary, adrenal and other organs are also affected. Injecting thyroid extracts prevents these effects from taking place.

The effects of giving an overdose of extract to an intact animal may also be observed, and if the suspected action of the gland is added to, this is additional evidence. Having obtained an extract, attempts should be made to isolate from it a substance that will produce the same effects as the whole extract in an animal from which the organ has been removed. If possible the substance should be identified chemically, in which case it may be possible to synthesise it and study its actions more precisely. Also it should be obtained from the gland or the bloodstream in concentrations sufficient to produce an effect in the normal living animal. The concentrations of the suspected substance in the artery carrying blood to the organ, and in the vein carrying blood away, may be measured and compared. If the concentration in the vein is highest, this is good evidence that the organ is producing the substance. Removal of part of an organ may result in a drop in the breakdown products from the 'hormone' in the urine: this can be measured. A similar drop may be produced by disease.

Analysis of experimental results must be performed with care. For example, large overdoses of a hormone may produce an effect opposite to that of the hormone in low or normal concentrations, and the removal of one organ may be compensated for by the increased activity of another. In some cases two organs are so intimately connected (e.g. in the frog the adrenal tissue is dispersed throughout the kidney) that it is not possible to remove the one and then to make up for its removal by injecting extracts. Lastly it must be remembered that just because a hormone is active in one animal it does not follow that the same hormone has an effect in the human.

CHAPTER TWENTY-EIGHT

The Pituitary – Master Gland

THE pituitary gland is a tiny, almost egg-shaped structure about half an inch long by a third of an inch across in man. It weighs about 0.5 gram ($\frac{1}{60}$ ounce). Yet the many hormones that it produces have such numerous and important effects that it is rightly called the *master gland*.

These hormones affect growth and metabolism (the sum total of the chemical reactions within the body), particularly that of proteins, fats and carbohydrates; they control water and salt loss through the kidney, the sex glands, thyroid and adrenals, and have an effect on the smooth muscle in the walls of the blood vessels. Another important effect is that of stimulating

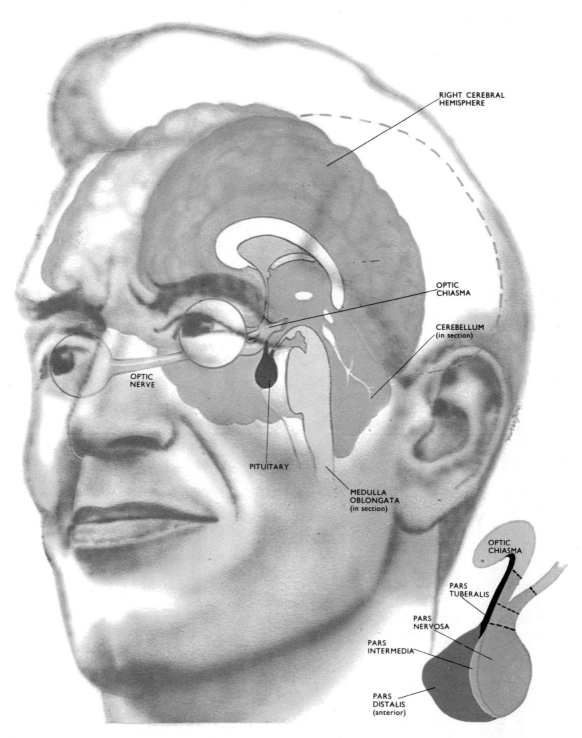

RIGHT CEREBRAL
HEMISPHERE

OPTIC
CHIASMA

CEREBELLUM
(in section)

OPTIC
NERVE

PITUITARY

MEDULLA
OBLONGATA
(in section)

OPTIC
CHIASMA

PARS
TUBERALIS

PARS
NERVOSA

PARS
INTERMEDIA

PARS
DISTALIS
(anterior)

In man the pituitary gland is situated just beneath the optic chiasma, (inset) a diagram showing the major divisions of the gland.

the muscle in the wall of the uterus during the birth process.

However, it must be stressed that the pituitary gland is not quite the master gland that it would appear to be from the above description. Many of the endocrine glands are not under its control while its control of others is only that of adjusting the rate at which they produce their own hormones. Removal of the pituitary does not prevent them from secreting these hormones. It must also be stressed that the pituitary is itself acted upon by other endocrines. For example the rate at which it produces the hormone that acts on the thyroid (the so-called *thyrotropic* hormone) varies with the

(*left*) *In a child overproduction of growth hormone results in gigantism,* (*right*) *underproduction of the hormone produces a pituitary dwarf.*

rate at which the thyroid is working. Thus, when the thyroid is producing less hormone than it should be, the pituitary releases more of its thyrotropic hormone and so hormone production in the thyroid is speeded up. This 'see-saw' or reciprocal relationship between the pituitary and other structures is characteristic of many of the body processes. In such a way the 'steady state' is maintained.

Structure

The pituitary gland is suspended from the underside of the brain by a thin stalk lying just below the point where the fibres of the optic nerves cross (i.e. the *optic chiasma*). Reddish-grey in colour, it is formed partly from the floor of the brain and partly from the roof of the mouth.

The pituitary may be divided into two main lobes, a front or *anterior* lobe and a hind or *posterior* lobe. It may be sub-divided into a *pars distalis* (anterior) and *pars tuberalis*, *pars intermedia* and *pars nervosa* forming the posterior lobe.

The anterior part of the pituitary is so distinct from the remainder of the gland that it is convenient to consider it separately. The hormones that it produces are all proteins. Between them they probably affect most of the other cells in the body. They fall readily into two main groups (1) those having an effect on *growth* and *metabolism*, (2) those that influence the *adrenals* and the *gonads*.

A *growth* hormone has been isolated. It plays an essential part in the normal growth of the body. Overproduction of the hormone through an abnormality of the pituitary produces gigantism and acromegaly (bone thickening). Loss of function of the anterior pituitary in young mammals produces dwarfs. Conversely injection of overdoses of growth hormone in young animals produces giants.

Growth hormone also affects the glands of the digestive system that secrete the digestive enzymes. It opposes some of the actions of the adrenals, encourages the body cells to retain nitrogen, and speeds up the burning of fat.

Another hormone released by the anterior pituitary is the *thyrotropic* hormone. (*Tropic* hormones act on specific organs only – the names of particular hormones are made up from part of the name of the gland on which they act, and '*tropic*' meaning to 'seek' – trophic is also used but means 'nourish'). The thyrotropic hormone acts on the thyroid gland stimulating its cells to secrete. Thyroid hormone governs the general metabolism of the body cells. *Prolactin*, another anterior pituitary hormone, causes the production of milk in the mammary glands after these have been 'prepared' by the action of hormones released by the ovary.

The other hormones released by the anterior pituitary affect either the sex glands or the adrenals. The adrenal gland plays a prominent part in preparing the body to cope with unusual conditions (*stress*), such as extensive heat or cold. Part of the gland (*medulla*) produces adrenaline, whilst the rest (*cortex*) produces a number of hormones. When extreme conditions are encountered, the adrenal medulla is stimulated into producing adrenaline. This is carried in the blood to the pituitary which is perhaps in this way caused to release the hormone that affects the adrenal cortex. This hormone is called the *adrenocorticotropic* hormone, or ACTH for short. ACTH stimulates the adrenal cortex to release its hormones. These have a number of effects in different parts of the body – particularly on the parts that have a protective and adjusting role.

Two major hormones produced by the anterior lobe act on the sex glands. One stimulates the production of eggs in the ovaries of the female or sperm in the testes of the male. The other causes the development of a special tissue in the spaces left after the eggs have been discharged from the ovaries. This tissue – *corpus luteum* – is particularly important in producing *progesterone*, a hormone that stimulates the development of the womb lining in the menstrual cycle, and, if a fertilized egg is implanted there, in the later development of the placenta through which the growing embryo is nourished.

Our present knowledge indicates that the posterior part of the pituitary has three main activities produced by two hormones. One, *oxytocin* (*or pitocin*), causes the womb (*uterus*) to contract. It is thought that this action is extremely important at birth in assisting the passage of the young out of the uterus. In experiments, oxytocin has also caused an increase in the supply of milk by the mammary glands to the suckling young. It is not certain what part oxytocin plays in this respect in life.

The second hormone produced by the posterior pituitary is *vasopressin*. Its effect on the blood system is slight, injections causing the smooth muscle of the blood vessel walls to contract. Its normal role in man is not certain. However, another effect is well established, that of controlling the loss of water and salt in the urine. Water loss is known as *diuresis*. Vasopressin acts on the kidneys causing them to reabsorb more water from the urine – it reduces water loss – and it is known therefore, as the *antidiuretic* hormone (against diuresis). Its shortened name is A.D.H.. A.D.H. promotes the retention of water by the kidney tubules but at the same time it causes a greater loss of salt. Cells in the part of the brain above the pituitary (*the hypothalamus*) are sensitive to the salt concentration in the blood. Special nerve cells of the hypothalamus probably produce the A.D.H. and it passes to the posterior pituitary along the nerve fibres, being released when required into the blood capillaries there. Such a transport of stimulating material along nerve fibres is called *neurosecretion*.

Failure of the pituitary to produce A.D.H. in sufficient quantities causes the disease *diabetes insipidus* when as much as thirty-five pints of water may be lost per day in the urine. It is interesting that the level of A.D.H. in the blood of the Kangaroo rat, that lives in deserts, is eight times as high as that of a dog. Consequently the former produces very much more concentrated urine.

CHAPTER TWENTY-NINE

The Adrenal Glands

LOOSELY attached to the upper side of each kidney there is a small yellowish mass of glandular tissue. This is the *adrenal* gland, also called the *supra-renal* gland. Although the combined weight of the adrenals is less than one ounce in an adult man, these glands play a very important part in the regulation of the body's activity.

Each adrenal is actually composed of two distinct parts, a central *medulla* and an outer, slightly larger, *cortex*.

The Adrenal Medulla

This, the central part of the adrenal gland, is derived from the embryonic nervous tissue and resembles nerve tissue in its action. The nerves supplying the medulla actually make contact with the cells and control their secretion. The main substance produced by the medulla is called *adrenaline* (or *epinephrine*). It is released, in response to nervous signals, when one experiences a sudden fright or mounting excitement. The action of adrenaline on the body is similar to that of the sympathetic nerves (those nerves that 'subconsciously' control the working of the gut, blood system, and other internal organs).

When adrenaline is released into the blood it is carried round the body and acts very rapidly. It causes the blood vessels supplying the skin and the gut to contract. This reduction in blood supply is responsible for the pale colour of a frightened person, and for the 'empty' feeling in the stomach. Blood vessels to the muscles enlarge under the action of adrenaline, and the heart-beat is accelerated. The liver is caused to release extra sugar into the blood and contraction of the spleen adds extra red corpuscles to the blood-stream. The result of all this is to reduce the rate of activities such as digestion but to allow the muscles and brain more fuel (sugar) and oxygen. The body is thus prepared to meet any sudden strain that might be imposed. For example, the action of adrenaline can be experienced through the increased heart-beat just prior to a big occasion (e.g. a race), or if one is forced to brake hard when driving a car.

The Adrenal Cortex

This organ also aids the body in adapting itself to undue strain or stress but the action in this case is not immediate. The cortex originates from the wall of the body cavity, close to the origin of the kidney. It is made up of groups and strings of cells containing large numbers of fatty droplets. The cortex is not like the nervous tissue of the medulla. If part of the cortex is removed, it will regenerate and regain its normal size. This does not happen with the medulla. The cortex is more important to life than the medulla for its secretions control much of the body's normal activity. The secretions of the cortex are fatty substances known as *steroids*. The mechanisms by which these substances act are not clearly understood,

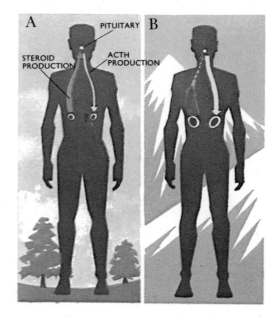

Under normal conditions (A) there is a delicate balance between the secretions of the pituitary and those of the adrenal cortex. When the body is exposed to abnormal stress (B) the tissues require more steroids and less reach the pituitary. More ACTH is then released and causes growth of the adrenals and greater steroid production.

Mounting tension in a cat when faced with a dog or another cat results in release of adrenaline. The latter acts on the muscles of the hair roots and causes them to stand on end

but they appear to be concerned with respiration and energy production in cells in all parts of the body. They are especially concerned with the metabolism of carbohydrates and with the balance of inorganic salts in the cells and body fluids.

The production of steroids by the adrenal cortex is not triggered off by nervous impulses but by chemical messengers (*hormones*) from the pituitary gland. The main hormone concerned is *adrenocorticotropic hormone* (hereafter called ACTH). In a healthy person there is a delicate balance between the supply and demand of steroids from the cortex. The cells need more or less steroids according

99

to the conditions. Prolonged cold, low air pressure, pregnancy, illness and many other features, all alter the demand for steroids.

If there is more than the necessary amount of steroids in the blood, they will not all be used. Steroids returning in the blood to the pituitary will prevent the production of ACTH and thus the production of more steroids will be halted. Similarly, if not enough steroids are being produced, none, or only a low concentration, will reach the pituitary and ACTH will be released. This in turn causes increased production of steroids by the adrenal cortex. ACTH is also released by the action of adrenaline on the pituitary.

Adrenaline therefore not only prepares the body for immediate action but also helps in the preparation for longer periods of stress.

ACTH also induces growth of the cortex. If part of the cortex is removed (for example, during an operation,) the ACTH from the pituitary will induce the adrenal cortex to grow until it is back to its original size. Also, if one complete adrenal ceases to function, the other will grow until it is large enough to produce enough steroids for the two glands.

Without any adrenals there can be no adaptation to unusual conditions or strain, but life can be prolonged by injection of cortical steroids.

CHAPTER THIRTY

The Thyroid Gland

FOR a hundred years or more it has been apparent that such conditions as goitre (enlargement of the thyroid gland) and cretinism are particularly common in certain inland or mountainous regions of the world – for example, the Himalayan plateau, the Alpine region of Europe, the Andean plateau in South America, states bordering the Rockies and the Great Lakes of North America, and Derbyshire in Britain. Certainly a major factor in the cause of such thyroid abnormalities would appear to be lack of the necessary amount of iodine in the soil. The explanation for this is that most of the iodine in the soil of mountainous and inland areas has been leached out and carried to the sea. This idea is supported by the fact that the incidence of goitres is lower in areas close

to the sea. Furthermore, tests show the soil, and vegetables that grow there, to contain greater amounts of iodine.

The association of a lack of iodine in the diet with abnormality of the thyroid gland provides an important clue to its role in the body. We now know that the thyroid is concerned with the metabolism of iodine to a greater extent than any other part of the body. Its function is to incorporate the iodine supplied in the diet into large organic molecules – the *thyroid hormones* – whose action affects all other parts of the body from the time that it develops in the unborn child.

The thyroid gland is an 'H'-shaped structure situated in the neck, in front of the windpipe and under the 'Adam's apple' or thyroid cartilage. The 'H' consists of a right and left lobe connected by a narrow isthmus. It is approximately one and a half inches in height, about one inch across and four fifths of an inch deep. It has an extremely rich blood supply. The tissue of the gland is mainly made up of numerous hollow, spherical sacs or *follicles* whose walls are one cell thick. The cavity of each follicle is filled with a protein-like jelly known as *colloid*.

The colloid contains proteins, enzymes, the thyroid hormones produced by the cells of the follicle wall, and the compounds from which they are built up. The amounts of each that are present vary from time to time and from one follicle to another. The colloid is more than a reservoir, therefore. It is somewhat like a whole-

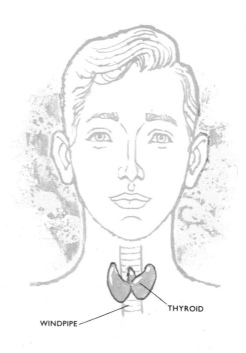

A diagram showing the position of the thyroid gland.

Much of the iodine absorbed into the blood from the food is taken up by the thyroid gland. When the gland is overactive it takes up excessive quantities of iodine. If underactive it takes in less than the normal quantity. In medical diagnosis the gland's activity may be determined by measuring with a Geiger counter the amount of radioactive iodine that has passed into the gland from a known quantity taken previously by mouth.

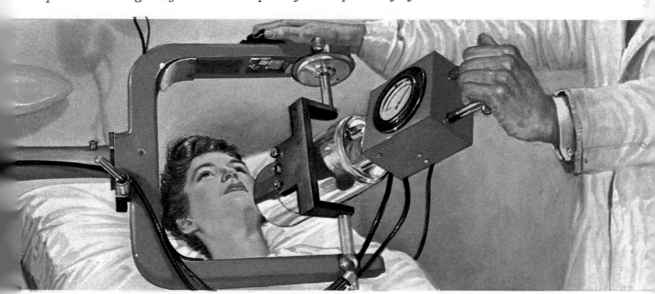

sale warehouse, always keeping a basic stock of numerous articles, some finished and others ready to be put together, the numbers of each varying as fresh supplies come in and as orders are despatched; and just as some supplies to a warehouse may be despatched as soon as they arrive whilst others may be stored to meet future demands, so the thyroid hormone may be released directly into the bloodstream or stored in the colloid. A feature better shown in the thyroid than in any other endocrine gland is the storage of hormone *outside* the cells that produce it.

Present knowledge indicates that the major hormone secreted by the thyroid is *thyroxine*. Its molecule is formed by the combination of two molecules of tyrosine (an amino acid) each of which has had two hydrogen atoms replaced by two atoms of iodine, with the elimination of alanine (another amino acid). A substance similar to thyroxine but containing only three atoms of iodine in its molecules is also produced and released into the bloodstream. This is called *tri-iodothyronine*. Though not produced in such large quantities as thyroxine, its molecules have a greater effect on the body cells.

Both thyroxine and tri-iodothyronine cause an increase in the rate at which chemical reactions proceed within cells by promoting the activities of enzymes. The oxygen uptake of the cells is increased in association with this. The thyroid gland has such an important role in the body throughout the life of the individual that abnormalities may have far-reaching effects. In a young child, if the thyroid fails to produce sufficient hormone, *cretinism* may result. The child is both mentally and physically backward. Lack of iodine in the diet may also produce the same condition. The thyroid receives insufficient iodine and so is unable to manufacture enough hormone. The production of too little thyroid hormone in the adult causes *myxoedema*. Common symptoms of this condition are thickening of the skin, which has a characteristically puffy appearance, increase in weight, the hair becomes coarse and brittle, and mental and physical reactions are slowed down.

Treatment of cretins, at an early stage, with thyroid extracts has largely overcome the defects in some cases. Startling results have been obtained with this treatment for myxoedema and complete cures effected. Cretinism may also be relieved by the addition of iodine to the diet.

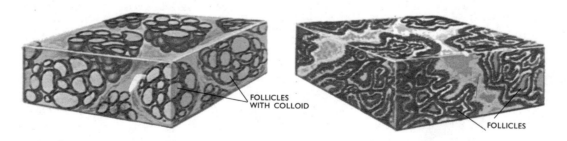

FOLLICLES WITH COLLOID

FOLLICLES

A block diagram illustrating the structure of the normal thyroid gland.

The appearance of the overactive thyroid gland. Note the infolding of the cell layers and scant colloid.

This picture of the thyroid is straightforward but there are puzzling facts that make it more of a jigsaw. For example, in myxoedema the gland may be enlarged, yet myxoedema is caused by underactivity of the gland. Enlargement (goitre) may also be due to lack of iodine in the diet and a further complication is that enlargement of the gland is often characteristic of an overactive thyroid. This may be hereditary or the result of a tumour. So-called *exophthalmic goitre* is one form of this condition in which the patient becomes irritable, nervous, his pulse is rapid, the eyes bulge and the skin may feel warm. A period of exhaustion and fatigue may follow this excitable stage. The patient is advised to rest and iodine may be administered for a short period prior to operation. This too is puzzling – why should iodine relieve both an overactive and an underactive thyroid? Even the administration of iodine after operation may aid complete recovery.

The activities of the thyroid are closely related to those of the tissues as a whole. The discussion above shows that the relationship is not a simple one. The pituitary gland is particularly important in controlling the thyroid. It produces the thyrotropic hormone which causes the thyroid to elaborate more thyroid hormone. The amount of thyroid hormone in the blood itself affects the production of thyrotropic hormone; a high level reducing its production, a low level increasing it.

An interesting finding is that there is a seasonal variation in the quantity of stored iodine present in the thyroid of such animals as pigs and sheep. The quantities are lower in winter and spring, when more heat has to be produced in order to combat conditions of stress, such as cold. The thyroid enlarges slightly during pregnancy, as well.

CHAPTER THIRTY-ONE

The Parathyroid Glands

THE parathyroids are essential for life. Though they are closely associated with the thyroid gland they remain separated from it by means of a connective cover or *capsule*. Usually there are four glands, two attached to each lobe of the thyroid, but the number may vary from a minimum of two to the known maximum, twelve. They are yellowish-brown in colour.

Each parathyroid is about the size of a split pea. Together their total weight is only 1/80 ounce (about 0·3 gram), yet they have a profound effect on the activities of other tissues. The parathyroids are particularly concerned with the body's utilisation of calcium, possibly also with that of phosphorus. Their removal leads rapidly to the continued contraction of the muscles (*tetany*), as a result of the disturbance of muscle and nerve fibres, and death ensues. Disruption of the normal working of muscles and nerves is largely due to the drop in the blood calcium level which follows parathyroid removal.

The parathyroid hormone (PTH) is probably a polypeptide (a substance made up of several amino acids) with a molecular weight of just under ten

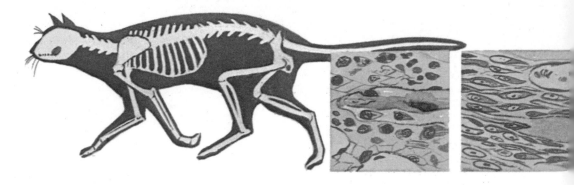

(left) A healthy animal moves normally, eats well and so on; bone growth is strong. *(extreme right)* an animal whose parathyroids produce too much hormone eventually becomes lethargic due to the increased

quantity of calcium in the blood. This extra calcium comes from the bony skeleton which loses large amounts. *(centre)* diagrams showing the appearance of bone

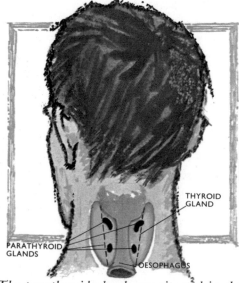

THYROID
GLAND

PARATHYROID
GLANDS

OESOPHAGUS

The parathyroid glands are situated in the neck behind and embedded in the thyroid gland.

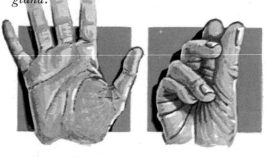

When insufficient parathyroid hormone is produced, blood calcium is lowered and the muscles eventually contract of their own accord (tetany). (right) parathyroid tetany, (left) hand held relaxed.

thousand, but no very pure extracts have yet been obtained. Because of this, accurate analysis of its role in the body is not possible at the present, though many experimental data have been obtained. Injection of parathyroid extract or of calcium relieves the symptoms that follow the glands' removal. There is a relationship between the size of the parathyroids and the amount of calcium in the diet. A low dietary calcium level causes their enlargement and conversely an increase in the level of calcium produces a reduction in their size. Milk is rich in calcium, and so it is not surprising that the parathyroid gland of a female mammal increases in size whilst she is suckling her young.

Recently it has been shown that PTH increases the absorption of calcium from the food through the wall of the intestine. It is interesting that the presence of vitamin D is essential for the absorption of calcium through the gut wall and for the proper formation of bone, for the parathyroid secretion also has profound effects on bone. The injection of PTH causes calcium to be removed from the bone and there is a consequent increase in the blood calcium level. The grafting of parathyroid tissue onto the bone

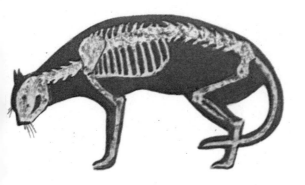

sections in a normal animal (left), and (right) in one that has received injections of parathyroid extract. The bone cells also lose calcium and become elongated and fibrous.

also causes the removal of calcium from the bone, but only in the region of the graft.

A large part of the body's calcium is found in the skeleton. Besides its structural role there and in teeth, and its part in the working of muscles and nerves, it is also necessary for the proper clotting of the blood. Calcium affects the passage of ions from one cell to another, particularly through the walls of the blood capillaries. Since calcium has so many functions it follows that the effects of the parathyroid are multiple, and hence abnormalities of them produce such far-reaching results.

CHAPTER THIRTY-TWO

The Pancreas

THE pancreas is a large pinkish-white gland situated underneath the stomach in the loop of the duodenum. It is really two glands in one. It consists mainly of an elaborate network of tubes or ducts, the blind ends of which are surrounded by fluid-producing cells. These release their secretions into the tubes which channel the fluid to the duodenum. This *pancreatic juice*, as it is called, contains several enzymes whose action is of major importance in the breakdown of the food into molecules that the body is able to absorb.

Interspersed like islands amongst this mass of enzyme-producing tissue are numerous patches of cells (sometimes almost two million), known as *Islets of Langerhans* after their discoverer Ernst Langerhans, a German biologist. The islet tissue has a rich blood supply but lacks any ducts. It produces the hormone *insulin*, which is released into the blood. It is this *endocrine* function of the pancreas that will be discussed here.

Early workers were interested in the digestive role of the pancreas, but, as so often happens, research on one particular aspect of a problem inadvertently leads to discoveries of great significance concerning another aspect. Johann von Mering and Oscar Minkowski, two German physiologists, had removed the pancreas from several dogs with the aim of observing any digestive abnormalities. They also discovered, however, that the urine of the dogs contained large quantities of sugar. Similar experiments confirmed these observations and so a clue to the non-digestive role of the pancreas was provided.

Researchers recognised that the symptoms produced in the dogs resembled those of humans suffering from *diabetes mellitus*. Clearly, an understanding of the nature of the canine condition might provide useful knowledge of the human disease. In 1922, Dr. (later Sir) Frederick Banting

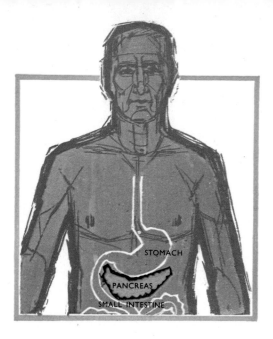

The position of the pancreas in man.

and Dr. Charles Best, in collaboration with John Macleod, showed that injections of pancreas extract could relieve diabetes. The active substance, 'insulin', has now been isolated in a high state of purity from pancreas extracts. It is a protein with a molecular weight of approximately two thousand. In the 1950's Frederick Sanger succeeded in establishing its chemical structure. Today many diabetics are kept alive by means of self-administered injections of specially prepared forms of insulin.

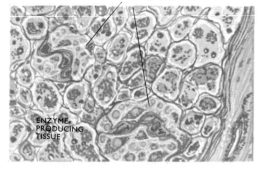

A section through pancreas tissue.

The presence of considerable quantities of sugar in the urine of diabetics suggests a relationship between insulin and the body's utilization of sugar. The sugar appears in the urine as a direct result of a high blood sugar level. The kidneys remove unwanted sugar from the blood and pass it to the bladder in the urine. Injection of insulin into a diabetic causes a rapid lowering of the blood sugar level, and continued injections will maintain this reduced level indefinitely. The abnormal metabolism of fat and protein common to diabetics is also corrected by insulin injection. In a diabetic person large amounts of protein, such as that of muscle, are broken down and converted into carbohydrates. This causes wasting of the muscles and leads to an increase in the blood sugar level.

Sugar, in the form of glucose, is the body's fuel. It is burnt in the tissues to provide energy for muscle contraction and the many building and repair processes that are taking place continually. The liver plays a central part in carbohydrate metabolism. It stores glucose in the form of glycogen – a carbohydrate whose molecules each consist of numerous glucose units. As the other tissues use up glucose, the level in the blood is maintained by the breakdown of the liver glycogen into glucose. Small quantities of protein and fat may also be broken down into glucose in the liver, and glucose in the food is absorbed directly from the gut into the blood vessels. Excess glucose in the food is stored by the liver. Insulin encourages the liver to produce glycogen. Its deficiency results in the overproduction of glucose by the liver and the consequent increase in the blood sugar level. The metabolism of fat and protein are also greatly disturbed and abnormally high quantities are broken down into glucose thus enhancing the effects due to the breakdown of glycogen. Insulin lack causes the overproduction of glucose, but it also seems probable that the cells are unable to use carbohydrate in its absence or when reduced amounts of it .are present. When insulin is deficient, protein and fat are broken down in place of carbohydrate as an alternative means of supplying energy. In a way not yet understood, insulin acts on the cells enabling them to use glucose for providing energy.

Adrenaline has the opposite effect to insulin. When it is liberated into the bloodstream (to prepare the body for action) it causes the liver to release extra glucose for muscular work.

Anterior pituitary extracts also have the reverse effect to insulin, causing the liver to release sugar. It is possible that the pituitary produces a '*diabetogenic* (diabetes producing) *hormone*'. Also the adrenocorticotropic hormone (ACTH), produced by the anterior pituitary, acts on the adrenals which produce hormones that cause a rise in the blood sugar level. This is due to the accelerated production of sugar in the liver from protein (not carbohydrate) and a reduction in the rate at which the tissues burn sugar.

Recently another substance, which may prove to be a hormone, has been extracted from pancreas tissue. This has been termed *glucagon*. Its effect is the reverse of insulin and the same as adrenaline. Acting on the liver it causes breakdown of glycogen and the release of sugar. Possibly the production of glucagon is a built-in part of the machinery controlling insulin production. Excessive insulin may be as harmful as insulin deficiency, if it leads to a low blood sugar. The cells, particularly those of the higher centres of the brain, have certain minimum requirements for sugar. If these requirements are not satisfied, the brain cells are unable to function properly and unconsciousness and death may result.

Very occasionally tumours of the pancreas cause excessive insulin production, a condition which may be remedied permanently by removal of the extra tissue, or temporarily by the administration of glucose.

Increase of the blood sugar level in the normal individual is immediately counteracted by increased insulin production by the islet tissue. The pituitary and adrenals also play a part in controlling the body's utilization of carbohydrate and it is likely that the cells of the pancreas receive nerve signals through the gland's autonomic nerve supply.

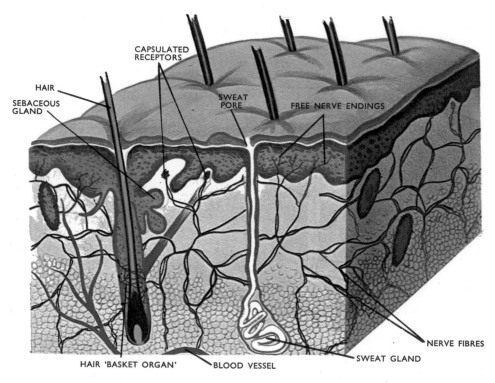

CAPSULATED
RECEPTORS

HAIR

SEBACEOUS
GLAND

SWEAT
PORE

FREE NERVE ENDINGS

NERVE FIBRES

HAIR 'BASKET ORGAN'

BLOOD VESSEL

SWEAT GLAND

A diagram of a block of human skin showing the positions of various receptors.

The Organs
of Sensation

CHAPTER THIRTY-THREE

Touch, Pain and Temperature

LIVING things respond to changes in their surroundings. Their success or failure depends on whether they make the right responses or not. Thus a flowering plant survives largely because its roots grow downwards into the soil to obtain a supply of water and minerals and because its stem grows upward, so that the leaves can obtain light and carbon dioxide for photosynthesis. In a similar way an animal's responses (at the simplest level) take it towards food and away from danger.

Higher animals possess special sense organs (*e.g.* eyes) and are able to make more precise responses. The response to a particular stimulus is not always the same, for in combination with the signals received from other sense organs and the store of information accumulated from past experiences, the 'set' actions of the animal are modified. This is particularly so in man. A top class tennis player will vary the shots he makes when in similar positions to avoid having his game 'read' by an opponent.

When asked how many senses we possess, most people mention only five – *sight, hearing, smell, touch* and *taste*. But in fact there are many more. These include balance and we are also sensitive to heat, cold, pressure and pain. Signals to the brain from sense organs in the gut signify the need for food and we are also aware of thirst.

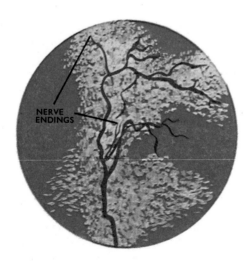

Free nerve endings in the skin highly magnified. These have no special capsules at their ends. They are probably pain receptors.

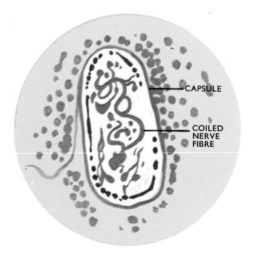

A coiled nerve fibre enclosed in a thin connective tissue capsule. Meissner's corpuscles have this construction and are found in the skin of the palms and soles and in the finger tips and tips of the toes.

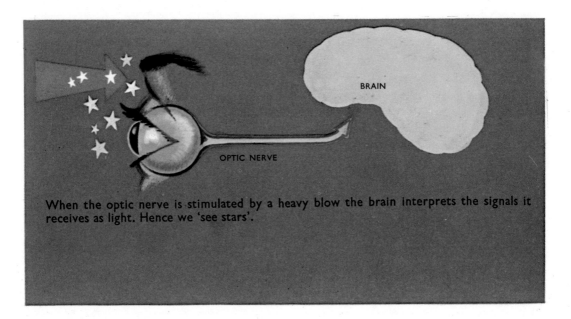

When the optic nerve is stimulated by a heavy blow the brain interprets the signals it receives as light. Hence we 'see stars'.

Some biologists dispute whether there are separate structures for some of these senses. They suggest that the handling of the receptors during their preparation (staining, etc.) may produce structural differences and they prefer the idea that the interpretation of a stimulus depends on which nerve tract carries the signals to the central nervous system. Thus when the endings of the optic nerve are stimulated the signals that pass to the brain are always interpreted as light. That is why we sometimes 'see stars' when we receive a heavy blow on the head. The blow stimulates the optic nerve and the brain interprets the signals it receives as light.

The simple receptors for the senses described are indeed simple in structure compared with those for sight (the eyes) and those for hearing and balance (the ear). Besides the semicircular canals in the ear, special nerve endings (the spindle organs) in the muscles are concerned with the body's balance.

The skin is richly supplied with receptors. This is of considerable importance, for the surface of the body is in direct contact with the surroundings. If contact with an object is painful then a part of the body can be moved rapidly away before too much damage is caused.

Some areas of the skin are far more

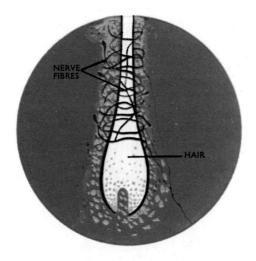

A hair-basket organ highly magnified. It consists of nerve fibres wrapped around the hair base. The nerve endings are stimulated when the hair is touched.

When a finger touches a hot object the normal reaction is for the hand to be quickly withdrawn (a reflex action). But if a hot valuable plate is picked up then the act of withdrawing the arm is often modified and we make an attempt to hold on to the plate by juggling with it until we find a suitable place to put it down.

sensitive than others. The soles of the feet, the palms of the hand, and the lips are particularly sensitive. Though the skin registers pain and is sensitive to touch, heat, cold and pressure, very few types of receptor have been identified. *Free nerve endings* have been found in all parts of the skin. The bases (*follicles*) of the hairs have nerve-endings wrapped round them (the *basket organs*), and the lower layer (*dermis*) of the skin contains coiled nerve fibres surrounded by a thin covering or *capsule* (*e.g. Meissner's corpuscles*).

Organs lying in the deeper layers of the skin are sensitive to pressure and vibration and it is thought that the *free nerve endings* are pain receptors. They respond to various stimuli – great pressure, chemicals, pin-pricks and extremes of temperature. Experiments show that definite areas of the spinal cord are set aside for nerve fibres that carry signals indicating

pain. When these fibres are cut, as may happen in serious accidents, the patient loses all sense of pain in the region of the body below the cut.

The simple reaction to pain is a reflex one – the affected part is withdrawn quickly and automatically from the offending object. But having had a painful experience in the past our muscles are controlled in such a way that an object known to be harmful is avoided.

There are also pain receptors inside the body. Various conditions – a duodenal ulcer, for example – give the sensation of pain.

By moving a moderately warm object or a cold object near to the skin numerous 'hot' and 'cold spots' can be mapped out. It is suggested that specific receptors are stimulated [though parts of the skin (*e.g.* that of the ear) lack receptors other than free nerve endings or hair basket organs].

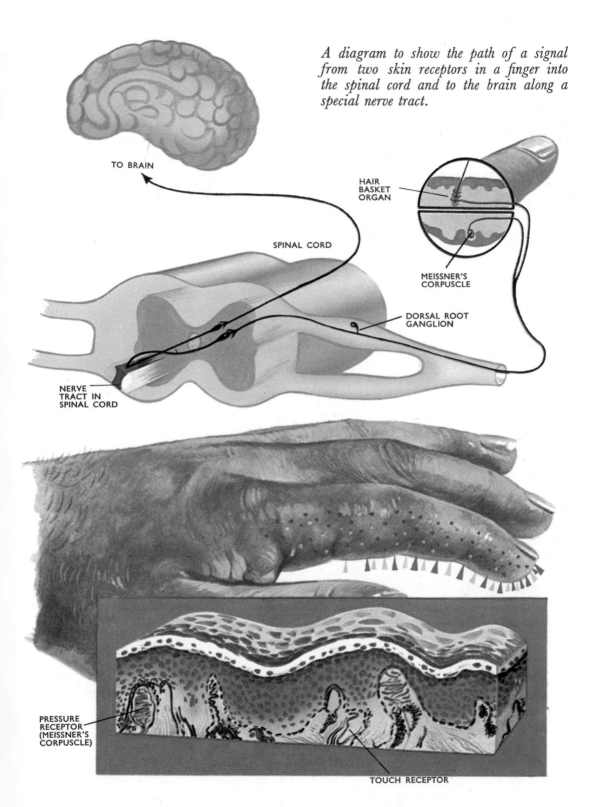

A diagram to show the path of a signal from two skin receptors in a finger into the spinal cord and to the brain along a special nerve tract.

TO BRAIN

HAIR BASKET ORGAN

SPINAL CORD

MEISSNER'S CORPUSCLE

DORSAL ROOT GANGLION

NERVE TRACT IN SPINAL CORD

PRESSURE RECEPTOR (MEISSNER'S CORPUSCLE)

TOUCH RECEPTOR

By placing hot and cold objects on different parts of the fingers 'warm' and 'cold' spots can be mapped out. The lower diagram shows a greatly enlarged portion of a finger and indicates the position of the touch and pressure receptors associated with the finger ridges.

Touch receptors are of several kinds. The ends of the nerve fibres of hair basket organs are very sensitive to slight movements of the hairs.

The tips of the fingers are well supplied with receptors. Two types have been identified, both associated with the ridges that leave 'finger-prints' (see illustration). *Meissner's corpuscles* are probably sensitive to fairly large disturbances of the skin, whereas the simple *Merkel's corpuscles* are stimulated by very light touch. Touch receptors on such parts as the lips are also highly sensitive.

Some of the receptors within the body are sensitive to chemical stimuli. The cells of the respiratory centre in the medulla are sensitive to the carbon dioxide concentration of the blood, for example. Signals from receptors in the lungs pass to the respiratory centre also. Signals pass from the *receptors* in the heart to the cardiac centre in the medulla and play a part in the control of the heartbeat. Cells in the hypothalamus are sensitive to changes in the blood osmotic pressure. Signals from them pass to the pituitary gland, which is stimulated into producing a hormone that acts on the kidneys.

The body, therefore, is equipped with a range of receptors, some of which respond to the slightest stimulus, while others are only stimulated by more intense stimuli. But when any are stimulated sufficiently, signals pass along nerves from them to the central nervous system. Within the latter the mass of information received from receptors can be acted upon immediately or stored for future reference. The system of receptors plays an important part in the integration of the body's actions.

CHAPTER THIRTY-FOUR

Sight

THE eyes, in man, play a particularly important part in the body's receptor system which provides the central nervous system with precise information about the surrounding conditions.

Each human eye is a hollow, spherical organ filled with fluid. The pressure of this maintains the shape of the eye. The eye wall has three main layers, a tough, fibrous outer coat – the *sclera;* a layer inside this containing pigment and blood vessels – the *choroid;* and an inner lining – the *retina* which contains the light sensitive cells, the nerve fibres leading from the retina to form the optic nerve, and nerve cells that connect the receptors and the nerve fibres.

At the front of the eye the three layers are modified. The sclera, which is visible as the white of the eye, is transparent and forms the *cornea,* whose outer surface is covered by a thin, transparent protective layer – the *conjunctiva.* The latter is a continuation of the eyelid lining. The choroid is modified to form the *iris* – the visible blue or brown pigmented part of the eye – which in its centre has an aperture, the *pupil.* The swollen outer part of the iris is the *ciliary body* which contains muscle fibres whose action changes the shape of the *lens.* This is a transparent crystalline structure which is suspen-

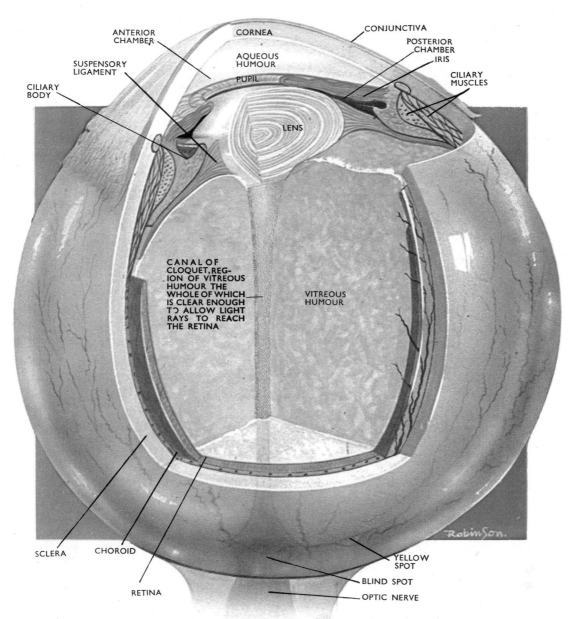

ANTERIOR CHAMBER
CORNEA
CONJUNCTIVA
POSTERIOR CHAMBER
IRIS
AQUEOUS HUMOUR
SUSPENSORY LIGAMENT
PUPIL
CILIARY MUSCLES
CILIARY BODY
LENS
CANAL OF CLOQUET, REGION OF VITREOUS HUMOUR THE WHOLE OF WHICH IS CLEAR ENOUGH TO ALLOW LIGHT RAYS TO REACH THE RETINA
VITREOUS HUMOUR
Robinson.
SCLERA
CHOROID
YELLOW SPOT
RETINA
BLIND SPOT
OPTIC NERVE

A drawing of a human eye magnified about five times and partly cut away to show its structure.

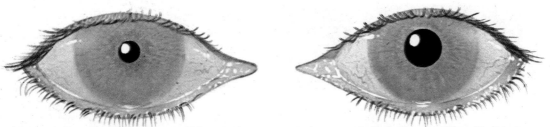

(Right) *In dim light the pupil is wide open to admit as much light as possible.* (Left) *In bright light the pupil narrows to cut down the amount of light falling on the retina.*

ded from the ciliary body by the *suspensory ligament.* The retina ends just behind the attachment of the suspensory ligament.

The iris and the lens divide the eye into *anterior* and *posterior chambers.* The front chamber, between the lens and the cornea, contains a watery fluid, the *aqueous humour,* and the hind chamber contains the thicker, more jelly-like *vitreous humour.*

Each eye is protected within its bony cavity or *orbit* in the front of the skull. The eyelids close together quickly when the eyeball is touched or when an object is moved rapidly close to it. By blinking every few seconds the eyelids bring down liquid from the tear glands. This action keeps the cornea moist, nourishes it and also washes away grit and dust. The eye is moved in its orbit by the action of six eye muscles. Those of each eye are co-ordinated, so normally both eyes are moved in the same direction.

Light enters the hind chamber of the eye after passing through the cornea, the pupil and the lens. The cornea forms an important part of the focusing mechanism, bending the light far more than the lens does. The latter produces a sharp image of the object on the retina.

The iris is equivalent to the dia-

phragm of a camera. It has two sets of muscle fibres, one arranged radially (in a similar manner to the spokes of a bicycle wheel) and the other in a circle in the inner part of the iris. The radial fibres contract in dim light enlarging the pupil and thus allowing as much of the available light as possible to enter the eye. Contraction of the circular fibres (the radial fibres relax at the same time) reduces the size of the pupil and cuts down the amount of light that enters the eye – as in bright conditions (in daylight the pupil is much smaller than it is at dusk).

The shape of the lens can be changed so that the images of either near or distant objects can be focused clearly on the retina. The lens consists of a 'plastic' arrangement of fibres surrounded by a thin capsule. The fibres of the suspensory ligament are inserted in this. If the tension on the ligament is altered the shape of the lens changes. When the eye is relaxed or looking at a distant object, the elastic force of the sclera pulls on the suspensory ligament and stretches the lens capsule, causing the lens to flatten and become thinner. When the eye is doing close work, the ciliary muscles contract. The pull of the sclera is resisted and the tension on the suspensory ligament is relaxed, thus allowing the lens to become fatter.

The structure of the retina is rather complicated. The light sensitive cells have their tips touching the pigment layer. Their bases connect up to ganglion cells which have connections with nerve fibres. There are also many cells with horizontal processes that connect up distinct receptor cells. The nerve fibres run over the inner surface of the retina

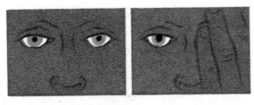

In daylight the pupils are small. When one eye is covered the pupil of the other widens as the result of a reflex linking up the two eyes.

and join up to form the optic nerve. Light entering the eye therefore has to pass through the retinal nerve cells before it can stimulate the receptors. The retina is said to be *inverted*.

Where the optic nerve leaves the eye there are no light sensitive cells. Light falling on this region is not perceived. Consequently it is known as the *blind spot*.

The light sensitive cells are of two kinds, called *rods* and *cones*. Most of the cones are concentrated in a small round depression, a short distance to the side of the blind spot. This is called the *yellow spot* or *fovea centralis*. The fovea is yellow because the cells of the retina at this point contain a yellow pigment. It is the region where the light is principally focused and only the part of an image which falls upon the fovea is seen sharply. This is because the cones are very small and set close together. They are sensitive to colour. The whole of the rest of the retina contains rods, sensitive

to weak light but not showing colour. For this reason we see no colours by moonlight. It is of interest that many nocturnal animals have few cones in their retina and some (e.g. bats) have an all-rod retina.

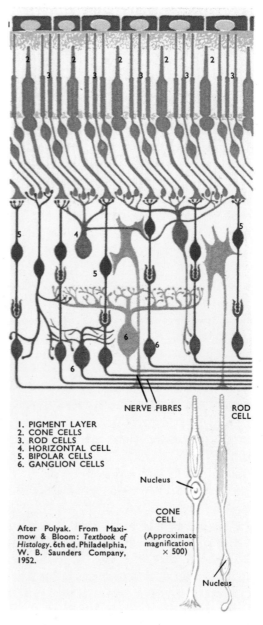

1. PIGMENT LAYER
2. CONE CELLS
3. ROD CELLS
4. HORIZONTAL CELL
5. BIPOLAR CELLS
6. GANGLION CELLS

After Polyak. From Maximow & Bloom: *Textbook of Histology.* 6th ed. Philadelphia, W. B. Saunders Company, 1952.

NERVE FIBRES

ROD CELL

Nucleus

CONE CELL

(Approximate magnification × 500)

Nucleus

BLOOD VESSELS

YELLOW SPOT

BLIND SPOT

A diagram showing the distribution of rods (white) and cones (dark) in the retina.

A section through the human retina shown schematically and greatly enlarged. Also, drawings of a rod and a cone cell.

The sensitivity to light depends upon the pigment *visual purple* in the ends of the receptor cells. When light falls on the retina visual purple undergoes chemical change. It is thought that its breakdown into other compounds stimulates the rods and so signals pass from them by way of the ganglion cells to fibres of the optic nerve and hence to the brain. The latter interprets these signals as light. In the dark the chemical change is reversed and visual purple is reconstituted. Presumably a similar chemical change stimulates the cones, though no substance has positively been shown to undergo such a change.

CHAPTER THIRTY-FIVE

Seeing in Depth and Colour

HUMANS have *binocular* vision. The eyes are in the front of the head and their fields of view overlap. The brain interprets the two slightly different sets of signals that it receives from the eyes as one composite picture. The nerve fibres from the right half of each retina pass to the right side of the brain. Those from the left halves pass to the left side of the brain. Presumably fibres from corresponding parts of each retina pass to the same part of the brain. The stimulation of two corresponding parts of each retina results in a single sensation. Thus the combination of the two retinal images produces a single picture. When we 'look cross-eyed' at something the images of an object do not fall on corresponding parts of each retina. We thus see everything in duplicate.

It is possible to judge distance when using only one eye, but it can easily be shown that the use of two eyes together increases the speed and accuracy of this operation if a pencil is held vertically in one hand at arm's length. After closing one eye attempts are made to bring the tip of the index finger quickly from the side of the body to the tip of the pencil. If the experiment is then repeated with both eyes open it can be seen how much greater is the precision with which the tip of the pencil can be located. The eyes of man lie about an inch and a half to two inches apart so that a pencil tip (or any other object for that matter) is seen from two slightly different angles. This enables the position of an object to be judged with accuracy.

Colour vision

The rods of the retina are more sensitive than the cones. They thus respond to lower light intensities and are used in dim light.

The cones, because of their relatively low sensitivity, are better suited for vision in bright light. If a coloured object is moved slowly across a person's field of view when he is looking straight ahead it is recognised vaguely as an object at first. As it comes into his direct line of vision its colour becomes recognizable and it becomes more distinct. Since the periphery (outer part) of the retina contains rods only, the experiment suggests that the rods are *achromatic* (that is,

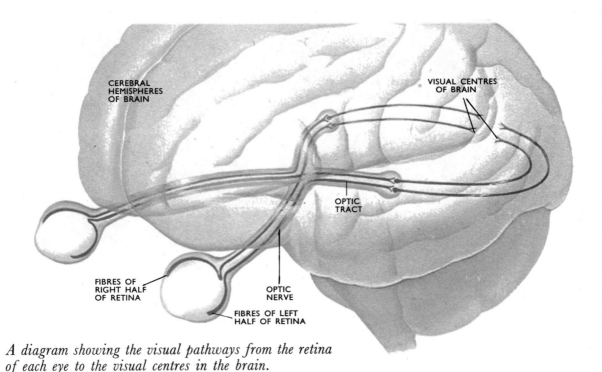

A diagram showing the visual pathways from the retina of each eye to the visual centres in the brain.

they are concerned with colourless vision) for when the object is at the edge of the field of view it is focused on the periphery. As it is moved nearer the direct line of vision so the image falls on more and more cones. This suggests that the cones are *chromatic*, *i.e.* they perceive colour. The cones are used little at night—

they are not sensitive to low light intensities. In very dim light we see no colour. Objects are seen as shades of grey. This is further evidence that the cones are the colour receptors.

Little is known about how the light-sensitive cells are able to discriminate between light of different wave-

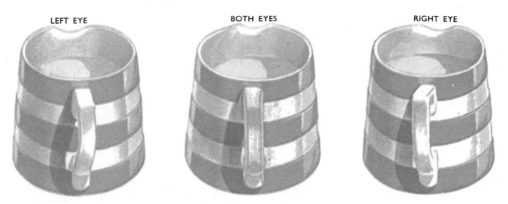

Each eye has a slightly different field of view. The differences in the two images enable us to perceive the depth of an object.

At night (left) *we see in greys and silver mainly using the rods. In daylight we see in colour using the cones.*

lengths even when their intensities are such that they would appear the same shade of grey to an animal lacking colour vision.

Most colours can be obtained by mixing lights of three primary colours, blue, green and red. For this reason Thomas Young (1772–1829) put forward a theory that there are three types of light-sensitive cells – each being most sensitive to one of the three primary colours. This theory was expanded by Hermann Helmholtz (1821–1894) and became known as the Young-Helmholtz

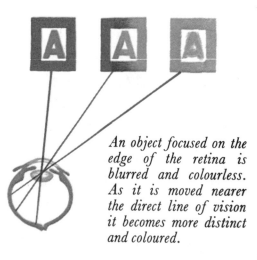

An object focused on the edge of the retina is blurred and colourless. As it is moved nearer the direct line of vision it becomes more distinct and coloured.

theory.

Other workers, noting that more exact matching of colours can be obtained by mixing four or more colours, proposed that there are more than three types of receptors. As many as seven are suggested by some authorities to be present in most vertebrate retinas. Granit, in Sweden, has performed experiments on animals that suggest that besides the receptors that are sensitive to narrow bands of the spectrum there are others that have a broad response. That is, they are stimulated by most parts of the spectrum. Thus if we look at a red object, those receptors that are most sensitive to red are the ones most strongly stimulated. A white object stimulates all the receptors and so we see it as white.

Recently Rushton, working at Cambridge, has shown strong evidence for the existence of colour-sensitive pigments in the fovea of man. Almost certainly two have been identified, one sensitive to green light, the other to orange-red light. A blue-sensitive pigment has not been identified.

Colour blindness

Few people are completely colour blind—that is unable to see anything in colour. Usually such people possess dim light vision only and appear to depend entirely on the rods. The cones are either absent or do not function. Others have dichromatic or two-colour vision. That is, they may be unable to see either reds or blues or greens. Most common is red/green blindness where red is confused with green.

Various tests are used to examine for colour blindness. In one, the subject has to look at successive pages of a book on which numbers printed in dots of various shades of one colour are on a background of dots of another colour. The numbers are visible to someone with normal vision but a colour-blind person cannot see them.

CHAPTER THIRTY-SIX

The Testing of Sight

THE first part of the examination is to see if the eye is diseased. The eye is examined externally with the aid of a magnifying glass, and then internally with an instrument called an *ophthalmoscope*. In the darkened room, the optician, standing quite close, uses this instrument to shine a beam of light into the eye. He looks through a lens system so that he can see the back of the eye very much magnified. The choroid, a collection of blood vessels, and the blind spot (the part where the optic nerve leaves the eye) can be seen in this examination and the picture he sees is known to the optician as the *fundus*. Blood vessels may show signs of high blood pressure. Any growths on the back of the eye can be seen or disease can be detected. Only a very tiny proportion of people do in fact suffer from eye diseases, and then it is a matter for medical treatment, usually in a hospital.

A record of visual acuity is made. It should be possible to read a

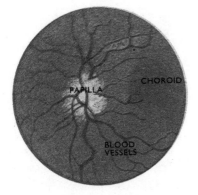
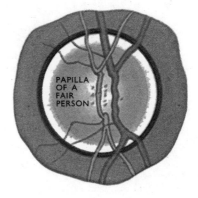

(*left*) *Normal fundus, as seen by the optician when he looks into the eye using an ophthalmoscope.* (*right*) *Enlarged picture of normal papilla (blind spot).*

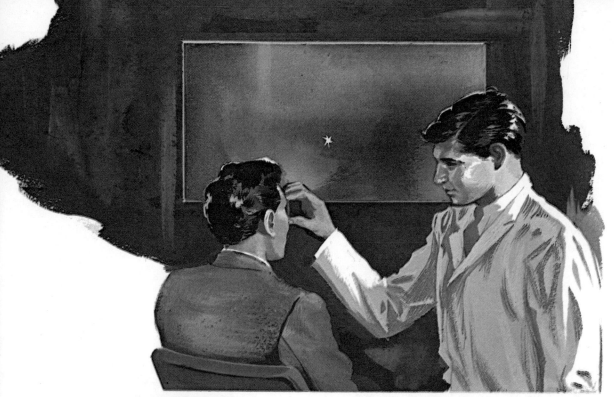

MADDOX ROD

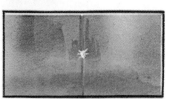

AS SEEN BY A NORMAL PERSON

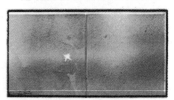

AS SEEN BY SOMEONE WITH FAULTY MUSCLE BALANCE

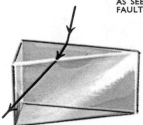

PRISMATIC LENS CORRECTS FAULTY MUSCLE BALANCE BY CHANGING THE DIRECTION OF THE LIGHT RAYS

Using a Maddox rod to test the co-ordination of the eyes. Here the right eye looking through the Maddox rod sees the spot of light as a red line whereas the left eye looks directly at it. If the eyes do not turn in sufficiently a prismatic lens is used to give the light the extra bending needed.

letter of a certain size at a distance of 6 metres. The patient reads the rows of letters, first large ones and then smaller, until it is impossible to go further. A normal eye has $\frac{6}{6}$ vision. A person who can read letters at 6 metres which should be readable at 24 metres has $\frac{6}{24}$ vision. For this card to be 6 metres away, a very long room would be needed. So that a room only 3 metres long can be used instead, a card with the letters reversed is situated on the wall behind the patient who looks at its image in a plane mirror on the opposite wall.

As the patient is 3 metres in front of the mirror and the image is 3 metres behind it, he is looking at an image 6 metres away.

The next stage is to make a record of the muscle balance of the eyes. When you are looking at any single point such as the point of a pencil, the eye muscles make the eyes turn in slightly so that they can both focus on the one point. The ability to do this is tested. The left eye looks in the mirror at the image of a point of light, whereas the right eye views it through a Maddox rod, a series of red glass cylinders which makes the point of light look as though it is a line of red light. If the red line passes through the bright point of light, then the muscles are acting properly; if it passes to one side of it, then the muscles may need the help of a prismatic lens. If the eyes have a tendency to wander apart, the prismatic or wedge-shaped lens allows them to do this while bending the light inwards so that both eyes seem to be looking at the same point.

The eye is able to see because it focuses rays of light from an object on to the screen or retina at the back of the eye. To do this, the incoming light rays must be bent. Most of the bending is done at the front surface of the eye but the final adjustment of this bending or refraction is performed by the lens. The examination of the eye for refractive error is one of the most important parts of sight testing.

An instrument called a *retinoscope* is used for this examination. The patient wears a spectacle frame in which different lenses can be fitted. The practitioner stands one metre away and uses the retinoscope to shine a beam of light, in which all rays are parallel, into the eye. By looking along the beam of light he

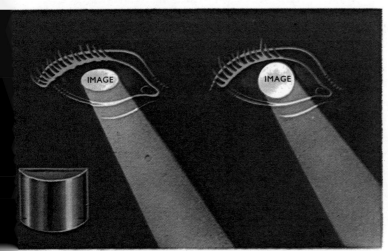

Images of a circular light source as seen on the retina using a retinoscope. Left: Astigmatic eye. Right: Normal eye. Inset bottom left is a cylindrical lens which corrects astigmatism.

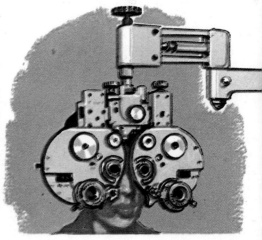

This modern instrument contains all the lenses the optician needs for sight testing. The patient is looking into a mirror on the opposite wall.

can see the image as a silvery disc on the back of the eye. If, when the beam of light is moved to the right, this silvery disc seems to move to the left then the eye is myopic or shortsighted. In long sight or hypermetropia the disc will move with the movement of the beam. By using lenses this disc of light is made to focus accurately on the retina and the optical error of the eye is corrected. Concave (diverging) lenses are used to correct short sight and convex (converging) to correct long sight. Now the silvery disc will appear without movement to right or left when the beam is moved.

But when an eye suffers from astigmatism the image is in fact slightly egg shaped because the eye has a stronger lens power in one plane (vertical perhaps) than in any other plane. This means that the vertical rays of light are gathered up more sharply than the horizontal ones and the silvery disc becomes oval. This is corrected by using a cylindrical lens (like a slice chopped off the side of a glass cylinder). This lens gathers up the rays in the direction where the extra bending is needed. The practitioner tests, using various cylindrical lenses, until he finds the one that makes the image at the back of the eye circular and free from all movement. These are not the spectacles the person will actually need as the test has been made at a distance of 1 metre and a correction has to be made for this.

CHAPTER THIRTY-SEVEN

Hearing and Balance

THE ear is not merely an organ of hearing: associated with the structures concerned with that function are parts which control the body's sense of balance. The receptors for hearing are stimulated by sound waves which cause disturbances of fluid in one part of the ear, and those for balance by gravity or movement (which moves fluid in another part). It is not so surprising therefore that the organs of balance and hearing should be connected.

Other receptors play an important part in the body's sense of balance. These are principally *skin receptors* in the soles of the feet and special nerve endings (*proprioreceptors*) in the muscles of the legs and neck, and the eyes.

The chambers and canals of the inner ear are filled with fluid. Pressure changes in the fluid of the coiled cochlea – due to movements of the oval window – affect the tiny sensitive hairs of hair cells on the basilar membrane. The hair cells are linked with nerve fibres and when the hairs move impulses pass along the fibres of the auditory nerve to the brain. This translates the signals as sound. In the semi-circular canals there are specialised patches of tissue containing hair cells. Movements of the head cause the fluid in the semi-circular canals to move and the hair cells are stimulated. Signals pass from them along fibres to the central nervous system which is informed of changes in the position of the head.

If a vibrating tuning fork is placed on a piano frame, to which the strings are attached, one string vibrates in

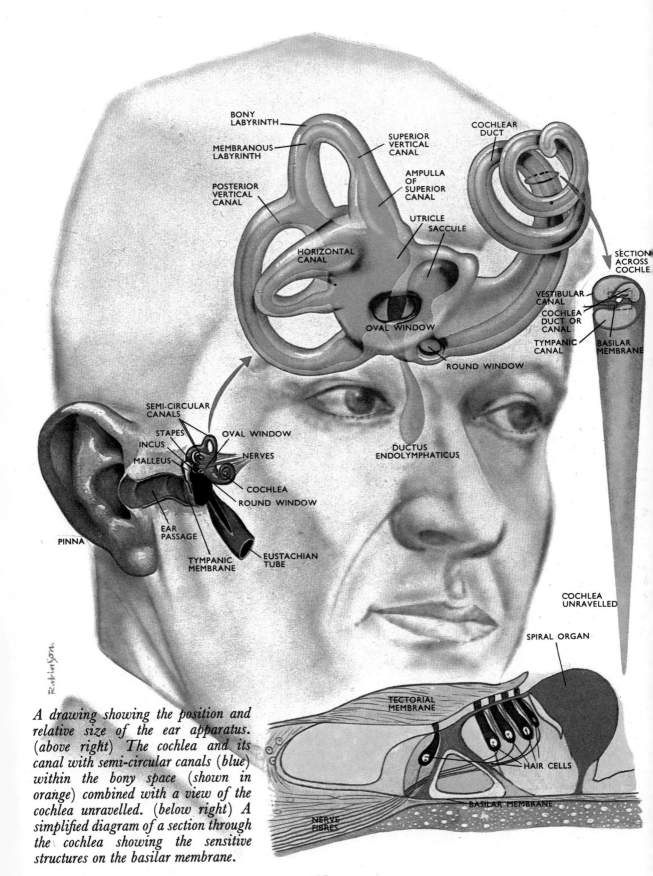

BONY LABYRINTH

MEMBRANOUS LABYRINTH

POSTERIOR VERTICAL CANAL

SUPERIOR VERTICAL CANAL

AMPULLA OF SUPERIOR CANAL

UTRICLE

SACCULE

HORIZONTAL CANAL

OVAL WINDOW

ROUND WINDOW

COCHLEAR DUCT

SECTION ACROSS COCHLE

VESTIBULAR CANAL

COCHLEA DUCT OR CANAL

TYMPANIC CANAL

BASILAR MEMBRANE

SEMI-CIRCULAR CANALS

STAPES

INCUS

MALLEUS

OVAL WINDOW

NERVES

COCHLEA

ROUND WINDOW

DUCTUS ENDOLYMPHATICUS

PINNA

EAR PASSAGE

TYMPANIC MEMBRANE

EUSTACHIAN TUBE

COCHLEA UNRAVELLED

SPIRAL ORGAN

TECTORIAL MEMBRANE

HAIR CELLS

BASILAR MEMBRANE

NERVE FIBRES

A drawing showing the position and relative size of the ear apparatus. (above right) The cochlea and its canal with semi-circular canals (blue) within the bony space (shown in orange) combined with a view of the cochlea unravelled. (below right) A simplified diagram of a section through the cochlea showing the sensitive structures on the basilar membrane.

125

The Path of Sound Waves

Sound waves are collected by the pinna (see illustration for the structure of the ear) and pass down the ear passage to the ear drum or *tympanic membrane*. This taut structure separates the outer ear from the middle ear, an air-filled cavity containing the chain of ear bones. These are the hammer (*malleus*), anvil (*incus*) and stirrup (*stapes*). The malleus is attached to the ear drum, which is made to vibrate by the sound waves. The movement of the ear drum is conveyed across the middle ear, by the chain of ear bones, to the *oval window* – a membrane stretched across a hole in the bone surrounding the middle ear. Beyond the oval window (to which the stapes is attached) is the *inner ear*. This consists of a series of spaces (*bony labyrinth*) within the bones surrounding the inner ear. Inside the bony labyrinth is the *membranous labyrinth*, a closed system of communicating sacs and canals. The membranous labyrinth is filled with a fluid called *endolymph*. It is surrounded by the *perilymph* which fills the bony labyrinth. It consists of two sacs, the *utricle* and *saccule*. Leading off from the saccule is the part of the inner ear concerned with hearing, the *cochlear canal* (or *duct*). This is a long, horn-like, coiled tube enclosed within the perilymph of the cochlea. In communication with the utricle are three *semi-circular canals*. These together with the utricle and saccule are concerned with the sense of balance.

The cochlear duct lies at one side of the cochlea and attached to a separating wall, the *spiral lamina*. This divides the cochlea into two, the *vestibular canal* and the *tympanic canal* which communicate with each other through a tiny opening within the tip of the cochlea.

The oval window is set in motion by the to-and-fro movements of the stapes. Its movements disturb the perilymph at the bottom of the vestibular canal. At the base of the tympanic canal is another membrane, the *round window*. The pressure changes in the fluid within the vestibular canal are transmitted down the tympanic canal. Each time the oval window bulges inwards (*i.e.* is pushed by the stapes) the round window bulges outwards. This is probably a safety device which provides pressure relief. The pressure changes in the cochlea affect tiny sensitive hairs on the *basilar membrane* – part of the spiral lamina. The hair cells are linked with nerve fibres. Movement of the hairs results in impulses being sent along the nerve fibres in the auditory nerve to the brain. This translates the signals it receives as sound. The ear does not hear – it merely receives sound waves which are transmitted as signals to the brain.

The basilar membrane is a band of tissue running almost the length of the cochlea – about one and a quarter inches. Arranged across it are a number of fibres, the lengths of which increase as the bore of the cochlear duct gets smaller. On top of these fibres is the *spiral organ* or *organ of Corti*. This contains the hair cells, the hairs of which project into a gluey flap – the *tectorial membrane* – which lies above them.

sympathy. According to Helmholtz's theory the movements of the fluid produced by a particular sound wave cause a small part of the basilar membrane to vibrate. Only the hair cells of this region are stimulated therefore. The arrangement of the fibres in the basilar membrane provides some support for his theory.

Work by Galambos and Davies has shown that different parts of the basilar membrane respond to different frequencies. For instance, when a narrow band of hair cells is anaesthetised, deafness is produced only over a narrow range of sound. But whereas Helmholtz suggested that each point on the basilar membrane is sensitive to a particular sound frequency, Tasaki has shown that the first coil of the cochlear tube contains receptors that are sensitive to sounds of high frequency (*e.g.* 8,000 cycles/second), the second coil to medium frequencies (*e.g.* 1,000 cycles/second) and the third coil to low frequencies (*e.g.* 500 cycles/second).

One point that is difficult to explain is how nerve fibres can conduct at the rate of 20,000 signals per second (most nerves conduct at below 500/second and the maximum is 1000/second). The range of hearing in man is for sounds of about 20 cycles/second up to 20,000 cycles/second. Obviously a nerve can cope with the lower frequencies.

The middle ear is in communication with the back of the throat by a narrow tube – the *eustachian tube*. This is normally closed by a small muscle but when we swallow or cough the tube opens to admit air to the middle ear from the throat. This mechanism ensures that equal pressures are maintained on each side of the ear drum.

The ear is protected from very loud sounds by the action of two muscles, one attached to the tympanic membrane and the other to the stapes. When these muscles shorten the tympanic membrane and the oval window (to which the stirrup is attached) become more taut so that the extent of their to-and-fro movement is reduced.

Balance

The parts of the labyrinth (other than the cochlea) are concerned with the sense of balance. Three responses are involved – *static responses*, *dynamic responses* and the maintenance of *tonus* (this is the resting tension in muscles; at rest muscles are not limp, they have tonus).

Static responses are concerned with maintaining the centre of gravity of the body on movement (*e.g.* if a frog is held in the hand and tilted to one side, its head moves in order that the eyes keep the same horizon). Dynamic responses are concerned with the body's movement when it accelerates rapidly in a straight line (as when going up in a lift) or in a curve (as when spinning round and round).

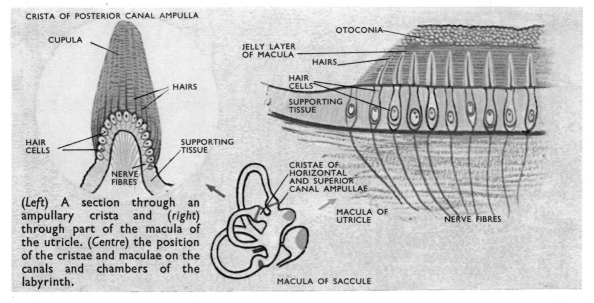

(*Left*) A section through an ampullary crista and (*right*) through part of the macula of the utricle. (*Centre*) the position of the cristae and maculae on the canals and chambers of the labyrinth.

Operating with the inner ear apparatus are the eyes, skin receptors in the soles of the feet, and the proprio-receptors in the toe muscles.

The three *semi-circular canals* are arranged at right angles to each other. They open into an oblong sac, the *utricle*. At one end of each canal is a swelling or *ampulla* within which is a ridge of sensory cells together with supporting cells, the *crista*. The sensory cells have hairs that project into a jelly-like mass, the *cupula*. Nerve fibres of the auditory nerve are intertwined round the bases of the hair cells. When the head rotates the fluid moving in the canals pushes against the cupula and the hair cells are thus stimulated. Signals pass via the lower parts of the brain to the eye, back and limb muscles which act to make amends for the head movements.

The utricle and saccule are in communication with each other by way of a narrow tube. Branching off this is a long blind duct, the *ductus endolymphaticus*. Parts of the lining tissue (epithelium) of the utricle and saccule contain a patch of hair cells and supporting cells (*macula*) like those of the canal cristae. The hairs of the former are embedded in a jelly-like mass though this is flattened. The jelly contains numerous small bodies consisting of calcium carbonate crystals mixed with protein. These are called *otoliths* or *otoconia*. They weigh the jelly down so that it is in firm contact with the hair cells. The maculae are upright but at right angles to each other so that each position of the head affects the hair cells in different ways. Signals from the sense cells of the maculae are

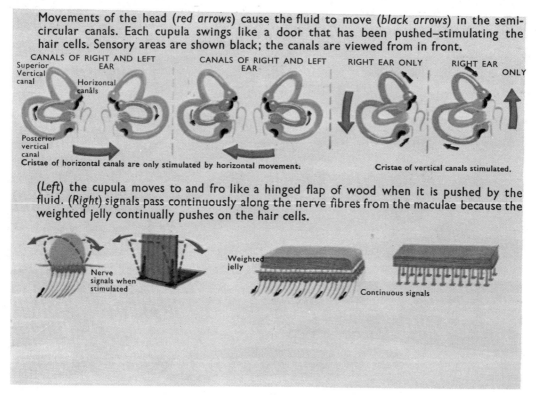

Movements of the head (*red arrows*) cause the fluid to move (*black arrows*) in the semi-circular canals. Each cupula swings like a door that has been pushed—stimulating the hair cells. Sensory areas are shown black; the canals are viewed from in front.

CANALS OF RIGHT AND LEFT EAR
Superior Vertical canal
Horizontal canals
Posterior vertical canal

CANALS OF RIGHT AND LEFT EAR

RIGHT EAR ONLY

RIGHT EAR ONLY

Cristae of horizontal canals are only stimulated by horizontal movement.

Cristae of vertical canals stimulated.

(*Left*) the cupula moves to and fro like a hinged flap of wood when it is pushed by the fluid. (*Right*) signals pass continuously along the nerve fibres from the maculae because the weighted jelly continually pushes on the hair cells.

Nerve signals when stimulated

Weighted jelly

Continuous signals

continuous and supply the parts of the brain that control the motor nerves with information so that these can maintain the state of muscle tone. The sense cells of the cristae, on the other hand, are stimulated by movement of, or pressure changes in, the fluid round the cupulae. They are concerned with dynamic responses.

When one is standing, information reaches the brain from a variety of receptors, ears, eyes – and so on. Pressure receptors in the skin of the feet are important suppliers of information. As the weight of the body is shifted from one foot to another or to different parts of either foot, different receptors 'fire off' and signals pass along nerve fibres to the central nervous system. As the limbs are moved, the tensions in the muscles change. This stimulates the *proprioreceptors* – specialised nerve endings of sensory nerves wound round muscle fibres or tendons. They are receptive to changes in the tension or the length of muscle fibres. Signals from them pass into the central nervous system and (by way of motor nerve fibres) out to muscle fibres along reflex pathways. In this way compensating movements are made automatically so that normally we retain our balance. When a muscle is pulled, for example, the proprioreceptors are stimulated. Signals pass from them to the central nervous system. Return signals cause the muscle to contract.

Proprioreceptors in the muscles of the head and the neck are also

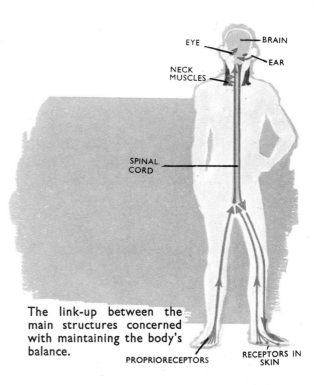

EYE   BRAIN
NECK   EAR
MUSCLES
SPINAL
CORD

The link-up between the main structures concerned with maintaining the body's balance.

PROPRIORECEPTORS   RECEPTORS IN
SKIN

important in providing the central nervous system with information on the posture of the body, the relative positions of its parts and their place in space. The actions of the head and neck muscles, in moving the head, alter the position of the eyes and ears. Thus the image falling on the eyes is changed – and the ear balance receptors are stimulated.

The balance of the body is maintained therefore by means of a complicated signalling system much of which is automatic. But the brain is informed of changes concerning the rest of the body and so is able to decide what the limbs or any other part will do.

CHAPTER THIRTY-EIGHT

Voice and Speech

THE voice is produced in the *larynx*, or voice-box, which is a special part of the wind-pipe in the throat. Around the larynx there are various

cartilages. Inside the voice-box are two sheets of tissue called the *vocal cords*. These are responsible for the actual sound production.

During normal breathing the vocal cords are relaxed and there is a triangular opening between them. During speech the cords are tightened by their muscles and as air is forced up from the lungs the cords vibrate. The opening between the cords opens and closes rapidly and sets the air vibrating with a fundamental frequency corresponding to the rate of vibration of the cords. This fundamental frequency determines the *pitch* of the note. There are also many *overtones* or harmonics produced. These are of less intensity than the fundamental note but of higher pitch. They give the note *quality*. A pure note, without overtones, sounds tinny.

Notes of different fundamental

Vowels and consonants

Vowels and consonants are the main speech sounds. Vowel sounds – whether they be pure or mixed – are produced with an open vocal tract and can be maintained. Consonants are interruptions of the air flow produced by closing the tract at the lips (the sound co*b*), at the teeth (co*d*), or at the back of the mouth (co*g*). These are *stop* consonants. If the tract is not completely closed, *fricative* consonants are produced such as the sounds 'v' and 'z' and 'th' (as in 'this'). The examples above are *voiced* consonants involving vibration of the vocal cords. Many others, both stop and fricative forms, are *unvoiced*. They are produced by air-movement in the mouth only. Examples are ca*p*, ca*t*, ca*sh* and *th*ick. Some sounds, such as 'm', 'n' and 'l', can be maintained and these are called *semi-vowels*.

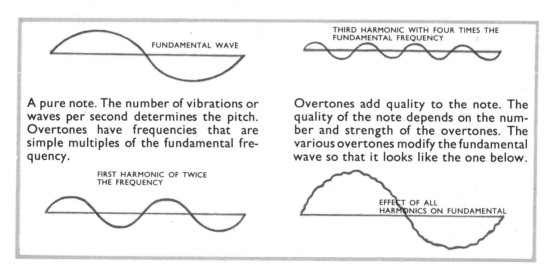

FUNDAMENTAL WAVE

THIRD HARMONIC WITH FOUR TIMES THE FUNDAMENTAL FREQUENCY

A pure note. The number of vibrations or waves per second determines the pitch. Overtones have frequencies that are simple multiples of the fundamental frequency.

Overtones add quality to the note. The quality of the note depends on the number and strength of the overtones. The various overtones modify the fundamental wave so that it looks like the one below.

FIRST HARMONIC OF TWICE THE FREQUENCY

EFFECT OF ALL HARMONICS ON FUNDAMENTAL

pitch are produced by changing the position and tension of the vocal cords. The volume of sound is controlled by the pressure of the air pushed through the voice box by the lungs.

A man's voice is deeper than that of a woman or child. This is because during adolescence the larynx enlarges (the Adam's apple gets bigger) and the vocal cords grow. Just as a double-bass produces a lower note than a violin, so the vocal cords of a man produce a lower note than the shorter cords of a woman or child.

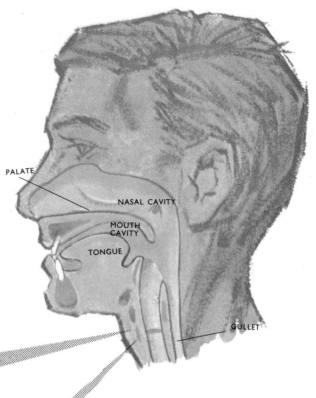

A cut-away diagram to show the position of the vocal cords and the resonance chambers of the mouth and nasal region. (Left) Views of the vocal cords from above.

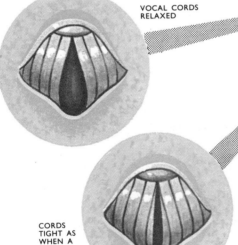

All mammals have this basic arrangement for making sounds although the size of the cords varies a great deal. The sound is produced in the voice box but its quality is determined by the mouth and nasal region of the breathing tract. These regions are cavities in which some of the overtones are lost, while others are emphasized. Man has fine control over his facial muscles and, just by changing the shape of the mouth, he can produce a very different sound. This is called *articulation*. The sound 'oo' is altered to 'ee' simply by altering the shape of the mouth. The vocal cords are still vibrating at the same frequency but a different set of overtones is being emphasized and the quality is therefore changed.

CHAPTER THIRTY-NINE

Taste and Smell

RECEPTORS that are sensitive to chemicals are called *chemoreceptors*. In man these are the organs of *taste* and *smell*. Taste receptors occur mainly on the tongue, a few elsewhere in the mouth and pharynx, and on the epiglottis (the flap of tissue that prevents food from passing down the wind-pipe). Small projections (*papillae*) on the tongue have flask-shaped *taste buds* scattered over them. These consist of groups of specialized cells that have nerve fibre endings between

tongue. An essential feature of both taste and smell receptors is that the chemical must pass into solution before it can stimulate the receptor. During dry cold weather the senses of taste and smell may be very much reduced.

By testing the reaction of different parts of the tongue to different substances it has been established that the greatest response for each of the four 'types' of taste – salt, sweet, acid (sour) and bitter – is in a different

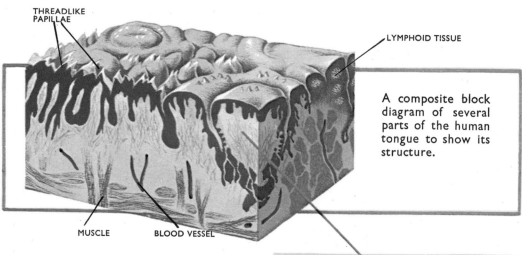

THREADLIKE PAPILLAE

LYMPHOID TISSUE

A composite block diagram of several parts of the human tongue to show its structure.

MUSCLE   BLOOD VESSEL

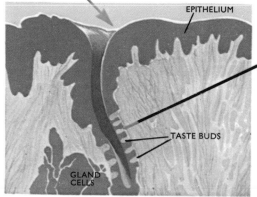

EPITHELIUM

TASTE BUDS

GLAND CELLS

them and wrapped round them. When the taste buds are stimulated, signals pass along the nerve fibres to the medulla. The taste buds are moistened by the saliva and by the fluids released by special gland cells in the region of the tongue. The tip is most sensitive to sweet and salty substances; the sides to acid substances; while the back of the tongue is most sensitive to bitter substances.

It is probable that there are different receptors for each distinct taste, but the most detailed study has revealed no differences in their anatomy.

Other points of interest are that some chemicals have different tastes when applied to different parts of the tongue, and the analgesic (local anaesthetic) cocaine has varying effects on the four tastes. The texture of food and its temperature (*i.e.* whether it is hot or cold) will also affect the apparent 'taste' of the food, for touch and temperature receptors in the mouth will also be stimulated by its presence. The taste of a substance is thus dependent on a number of factors.

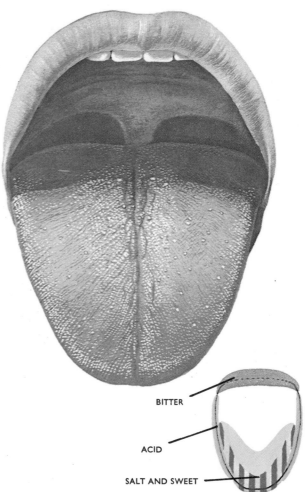

BITTER

ACID

SALT AND SWEET

A view of the human tongue inside the mouth cavity. (Inset) A diagram showing the areas most sensitive to the four taste qualities.

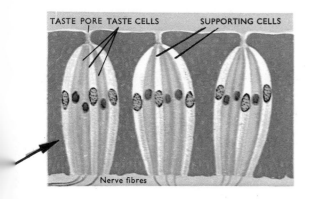

TASTE PORE TASTE CELLS   SUPPORTING CELLS

Nerve fibres

(Left) *A section through two papillae enlarged to show the position of the taste buds in the epithelium.* (Above) *A highly magnified view of three neighbouring taste buds showing the taste cells and supporting cells.*

Though the taste receptors are sensitive to minute amounts of chemicals the smell receptors can detect even smaller quantities. The basic tastes are inborn – automatic responses to particular chemical substances. This is perhaps reflected by the fact that the nerve fibres from the taste receptors pass to the medulla. In contrast the sense of smell depends largely on the store of past experiences (memory) and the nerves pass directly to the cerebral hemispheres. It is of interest that this highest region of the

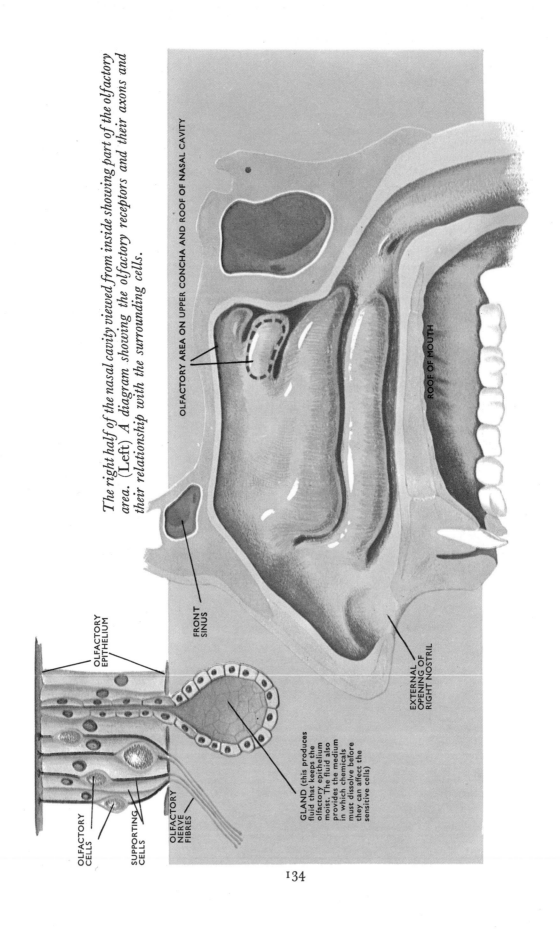

The right half of the nasal cavity viewed from inside showing part of the olfactory area. (Left) A diagram showing the olfactory receptors and their axons and their relationship with the surrounding cells.

OLFACTORY AREA ON UPPER CONCHA AND ROOF OF NASAL CAVITY

ROOF OF MOUTH

FRONT SINUS

EXTERNAL OPENING OF RIGHT NOSTRIL

OLFACTORY EPITHELIUM

OLFACTORY CELLS

SUPPORTING CELLS

OLFACTORY NERVE FIBRES

GLAND (this produces fluid that keeps the olfactory epithelium moist. The fluid also provides the medium in which chemicals must dissolve before they can affect the sensitive cells)

brain has evolved from the olfactory parts of the brain (those concerned with smell) of lower vertebrates.

We can of course appreciate 'tastes' or flavours other than the four basic ones, but strictly these are part of the sense of smell, dependent upon receptors in the back of the nose.

The smell receptors, together with those for vision and hearing, form the *distance receptor system*. That is, they inform us of conditions at a distance. The sensitive cells are embedded in the lining tissue (epithelium) of the nose, on the roof of the nasal cavity, on the upper part of the wall that divides the nose into two halves and on the upper fold (*concha*) in each half.

The olfactory (smell) cells are unique in that their axons pass *to* the central nervous system. (Generally nerve processes grow out *from* the central nervous system.) They are surrounded by supporting cells and glands. The latter produce a yellowish-brown fluid which moistens the ends of the olfactory cells. The chemicals to which the receptors are sensitive dissolve in this fluid. Its continuous production washes away chemicals that have already stimulated the receptors and so leaves them clean and prepared for further substances. All the olfactory cells have the same structure yet we can appreciate a wide range of smells. Whereas there are relatively few taste receptors and few nerve fibres from them, there are many smell receptors and numerous nerve fibres carrying signals to the brain. Within the olfactory parts of the brain the nerve fibres interweave and connect up with others in a most complicated way. It is possible that there are several different sorts of receptors sensitive to different smells. Since each part of the olfactory lobe receives impulses from a variety of receptors because of the elaborate interconnections, a whole range of different smelling substances can be distinguished.

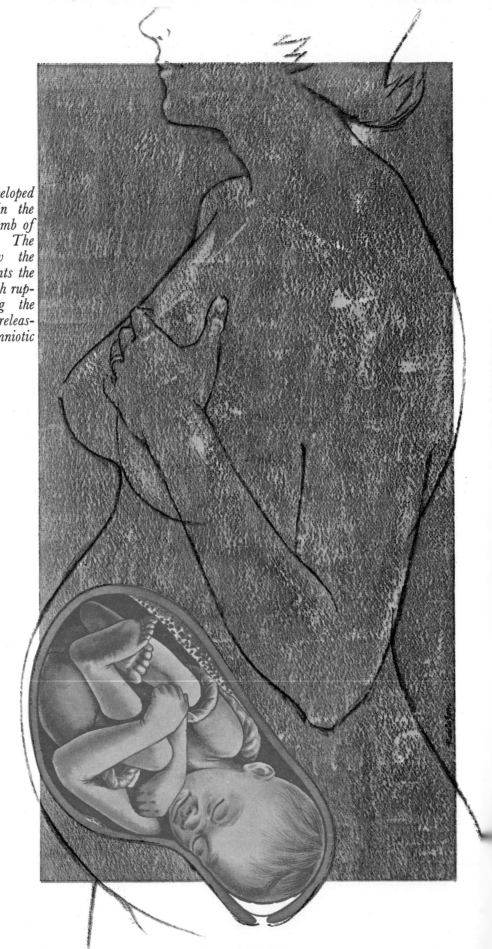

A fully developed foetus within the uterus or womb of the mother. The space below the head represents the amnion which ruptures during the birth process releasing the amniotic fluid.

The New Generation

CHAPTER FORTY

Reproduction in Man

IN placentals the reproductive system is well developed for fertilization of the egg within the body of the female and for its prolonged development there. Female placentals develop an elaborate organ, the *placenta*, provided for the protection and nourishment of the young during their stay in the womb or *uterus*. The human placenta is particularly well developed. It is formed by the fusion of certain embryonic tissues and the lining of the uterus. As the embryo forms, its connections with the lining of the uterus become more and more intimate. The layers of tissue between the blood vessels of the foetus and those of the mother are eroded away by the action of enzymes. Eventually only the walls of the foetal blood vessels and a small amount of connective tissue separate the foetal blood from that of the mother. The barrier between the two is very small, therefore, and the exchange of food molecules, oxygen etc. is enhanced.

The reproductive system of man is similar to that of other placentals. The paired organs (*testes*) of the male that produce sperms consist of masses of tiny coiled tubes. The walls of these *seminiferous tubules* produce the sperms. Each sperm has five main regions, an oval *head*, behind which is a narrow *neck*, leading to a long thin *body*, *tail* and *endpiece*. The sperms are of two kinds, each containing twenty-two chromosomes plus either an X or a Y chromosome. If one containing an X chromosome fertilizes an egg-cell (each of which has 22 chromosomes and an X chromosome) then a female results, and one containing a Y chromosome produces a male.

Fertilization thus produces a *zygote* containing the full complement of chromosomes, 44 plus 2 X's or an X and a Y. The head of the sperm contains the chromosomes whilst the tail beats actively when in the fluid (*semen*) produced by special glands of the male, enabling the sperm to swim up the reproductive tubes of the female to the egg. Usually only one sperm cell penetrates an egg cell but, to ensure fertilization, a large number are produced. Fertilization occurs high up in the egg-ducts (*fallopian tubes*) and the fertilized egg starts to divide as it passes down towards the uterus. Associated with the development of the egg within the ovary and its subsequent release (this is thought to occur on about the fourteenth day of the oestrous cycle), the lining of the uterus undergoes changes that prepare it to receive the fertilized egg.

The uterus lining thickens as the egg cell develops in the ovary. It becomes more muscular and richer in glands and blood vessels. In a woman the uterus lining continues to thicken – after the egg has been released from the ovary – whether fertilization occurs or not. If fertilization does not occur, the growth of tissue continues for a further fourteen days. It then breaks down and erodes away with the loss of blood characteristic of *menstruation*. Growth of the uterus lining and subsequent menstruation takes place

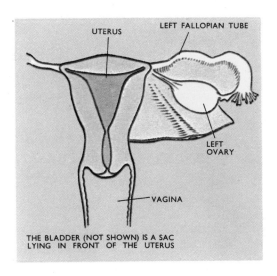

The reproductive system of the human fe-male (ovary and fallopian tube of right side omitted).

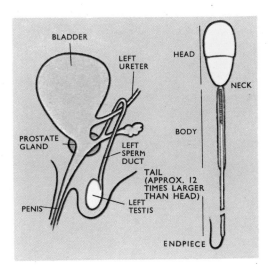

Male reproductive system of man, testis and sperm duct of right side omitted. (right) human sperm highly magnified.

regularly during approximately 28-day cycles. (There is a great variation between individuals, from 24 to 35 days). The first flow of blood (*menses*) occurs at an age of about 12 to 16 years and proceeds up to the age of 45 – sometimes up to 50 or just over. It is interrupted by successful fertilization

if the fertilized egg is accepted by the uterus.

The tiny fertilized egg or zygote, which contains the complete instructions for producing a new individual and for controlling its later life, has divided several times by the time it reaches the uterus. *Implantation* – the

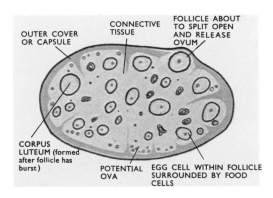

A section through a human ovary showing numerous egg cells (ova) at various stages of development within the follicles in which they grow. One ovum is about to be released from a follicle.

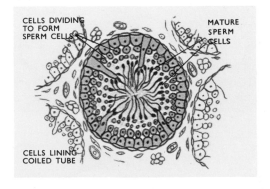

Each human testis consists of masses of tiny coiled tubes. This diagram of one tube in cross-section shows how the sperms are formed from the tiny cells lining the tubes.

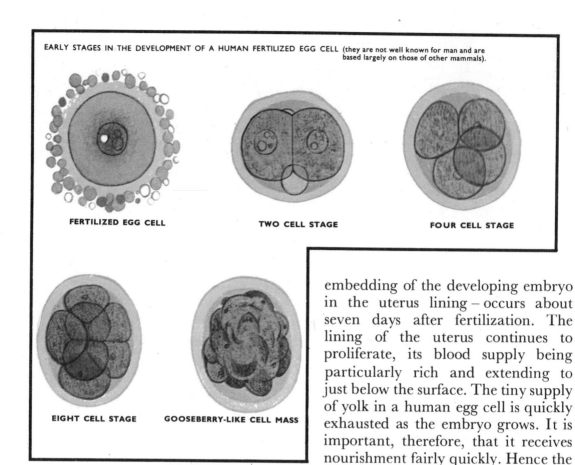

EARLY STAGES IN THE DEVELOPMENT OF A HUMAN FERTILIZED EGG CELL (they are not well known for man and are based largely on those of other mammals).

FERTILIZED EGG CELL **TWO CELL STAGE** **FOUR CELL STAGE**

EIGHT CELL STAGE **GOOSEBERRY-LIKE CELL MASS**

embedding of the developing embryo in the uterus lining – occurs about seven days after fertilization. The lining of the uterus continues to proliferate, its blood supply being particularly rich and extending to just below the surface. The tiny supply of yolk in a human egg cell is quickly exhausted as the embryo grows. It is important, therefore, that it receives nourishment fairly quickly. Hence the

7-DAY STAGE (IMPLANTATION OCCURS)

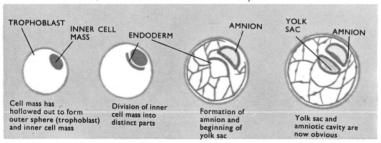

TROPHOBLAST INNER CELL MASS ENDODERM AMNION YOLK SAC AMNION

Cell mass has hollowed out to form outer sphere (trophoblast) and inner cell mass

Division of inner cell mass into distinct parts

Formation of amnion and beginning of yolk sac

Yolk sac and amniotic cavity are now obvious

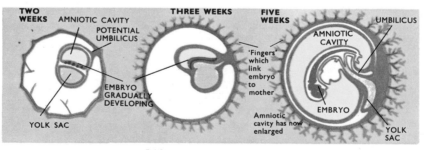

TWO WEEKS AMNIOTIC CAVITY POTENTIAL UMBILICUS THREE WEEKS FIVE WEEKS UMBILICUS AMNIOTIC CAVITY

'Fingers' which link embryo to mother

EMBRYO GRADUALLY DEVELOPING

Amniotic cavity has now enlarged

EMBRYO

YOLK SAC YOLK SAC

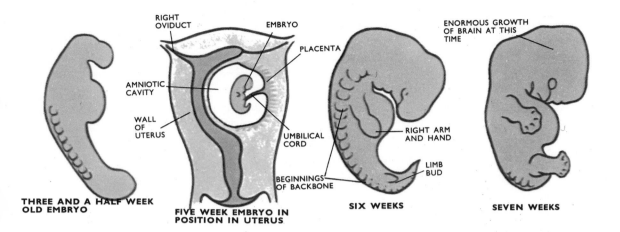

RIGHT OVIDUCT

EMBRYO

PLACENTA

ENORMOUS GROWTH OF BRAIN AT THIS TIME

AMNIOTIC CAVITY

WALL OF UTERUS

RIGHT ARM AND HAND

UMBILICAL CORD

LIMB BUD

BEGINNINGS OF BACKBONE

THREE AND A HALF WEEK OLD EMBRYO

FIVE WEEK EMBRYO IN POSITION IN UTERUS

SIX WEEKS

SEVEN WEEKS

importance of a rich blood supply being formed close to the surface of the uterus lining. The fertilized egg cell first divides into two cells, then four, eight, and so on, to form a ball of cells. By the time that it embeds itself in the uterus lining, it consists of two parts, an *inner cell mass* from which the young foetus grows, and a thin outer sphere of cells – the *trophoblast*. It is the task of the trophoblast to establish intimate connections between the embryo and the tissue of the uterus wall. This it does by eroding away the maternal tissues until only a thin barrier of tissue remains between the two blood-streams. The inner cell mass, which appears to consist of a number of identical cells in a ball, becomes flattened and soon begins to take on a more organised appearance. A thin layer of cells forms along its inner side. This *endoderm* soon hollows out to form a bag – the *yolk sac*. Mean-while the remainder of the cell mass hollows out to form a sac – the *amniotic cavity* – the wall of which is called the *amnion*. A network of cells surrounding the two cavities thickens above the embryo and forms a connection be-tween it and the trophoblast eventually becoming the *umbilical cord*, through

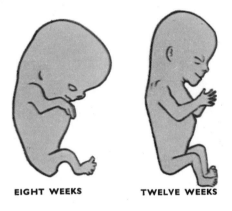

EIGHT WEEKS

TWELVE WEEKS

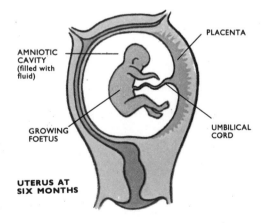

AMNIOTIC CAVITY (filled with fluid)

PLACENTA

GROWING FOETUS

UMBILICAL CORD

UTERUS AT SIX MONTHS

141

which food materials and waste matter pass between embryo and placenta. The amniotic sac grows enormously and is filled with fluid surrounding the embryo. This protects the embryo during its development.

By the time that the embryo is three weeks old, folds at the head end have curled over – the beginnings of the brain. Segments (*somites*) clearly show along the mid-part. These later form the body muscles and the vertebral column. As the embryo continues to develop it becomes more recognisable as a miniature human. Features such as eyes, ears, limbs etc., become more prominent and, internally too, many changes take place.

The period of *gestation* (time within the womb) in man is about two hundred and eighty days. The placenta nourishes and protects the embryo during the whole of this period. During the birth process the young child is expelled from the womb by the automatic contractions of the muscles within its walls, and usually also by the co-ordinated activities of the mother. The pains of giving birth have been considerably lessened in recent years by the use of anaesthetics. These act sufficiently to deaden much of the pain, but not enough to cause unconsciousness during the later stages of labour.

Following birth the umbilicus still connects the child to the placenta. It is ligatured (tied) and cut, and from that moment the infant is, in many respects, on its own. The lungs must function – it can no longer rely on receiving a supply of oxygen from the mother through the placenta. Similarly it must take in and digest food itself. It must get rid of waste itself and so on.

The reproductive processes in man, as in other mammals, are governed largely through the endocrine system employing chemical signals. The nervous system also plays an important part, however, receiving visual and other stimuli.

The pituitary gland is the centre of the chemical control system. Its hormones affect the whole of the reproductive system of both male and female. The placenta, testes, ovaries, and adrenals also produce hormones all of whose actions are closely associated.

Index